Walch Toolbook Series
Prose and Poetry
A Comprehensive Guide to Understanding Literature

Helen Ruth Bass
and
Diane Morrill

illustrated by Jane O'Conor

J. WESTON
WALCH
PUBLISHER
Portland, Maine

User's Guide
to
Walch Reproducible Books

As part of our general effort to provide educational materials that are as practical and economical as possible, we have designated this publication a "reproducible book." The designation means that purchase of the book includes purchase of the right to limited reproduction of all pages on which this symbol appears:

Here is the basic Walch policy: We grant to individual purchasers of this book the right to make sufficient copies of reproducible pages for use by all students of a single teacher. This permission is limited to a single teacher, and does not apply to entire schools or school systems, so institutions purchasing the book should pass the permission on to a single teacher. Copying of the book or its parts for resale is prohibited.

Any questions regarding this policy or requests to purchase further reproduction rights should be addressed to:

Permissions Editor
J. Weston Walch, Publisher
321 Valley Street • P. O. Box 658
Portland, Maine 04104-0658

1   2   3   4   5   6   7   8   9   10

ISBN 0-8251-3802-7

Contents

Premise . . . .*v*

Using These Tools . . . .*vii*

Part 1: Basic Tools 1

Senses 1
Person 5
Mood 7
Plot 10
Conflict 11
Style 13
Theme 14
Point of View 15
Slant 17
Setting 20
Character 22

Part 2: Figures of Speech 25

Figures of Speech 25
It Figures 28
Antithesis 30
Apostrophe 33
Hyperbole 36
Irony 39
Literary Allusion 42
Metaphor 45
Metonymy 48
Oxymoron 51
Personification 54
Simile 57
Synecdoche 60
Understatement (Litotes) 63

Part 3: Poetry Tools 66

Melody 66
   Alliteration—Assonance—Rhyme 66
Onomatopoeia 68
Rhyme Scheme 69
Rhythm 71
Stanza Patterns 76
Types of Poetry 80
   Epic 80
   Narrative Poetry 81
   Lyric Poetry 83
   Acrostic 84
   Ballad (Folk and Literary) 85
   Blank Verse 89
   Didactic Poetry 90
   Dramatic Poetry 91
   Elegy 92
   Epigram 93
   Epitaph 94
   Free Verse 95
   Haiku 96
   Light Verse 97
   Limerick 98
   Ode 99
   Parody 101
   Pastoral 102
   Satire 103
   Sonnet (Italian and Shakespearean) 104
   Wordplay 106
Explication of Poetry 108
Sample Questions for the Explication 111
Sample Explication Elements 112

Sample Answer Key *114*

Premise

Words are tools, and mastered words are power tools.

You have just had an idea. It may be that you have developed an outline for world peace, or you want someone to pass you the butter, or you have discovered the cure for our worst disease—but you will have to transmit that idea to someone else if anyone is to get any benefit from it. Suppose you decide to test your idea by asking me to check it out. The problem is that you can't just hand me your idea, like a block of wood. Ideas are very real, but they have no substance. To pass along an idea, you have to change it into words. The result is that what you give me will not be your idea, but a verbal description of your idea. I must then translate your verbal description into my interpretation of those words. The words are the tools we use to transfer thoughts.

For this transfer to be successful we have to speak the same language, so assume we both speak English. Even then, we have problems because so many words have more

than one meaning. Take the simple sentence "He passed." Did he throw a ball? Did he die? Did he score well on an exam? Did he hand someone a note? Was he playing cards? Was he driving a car? Just which "pass" is meant? Other elements will also affect our idea transfer. Consider the added complications of slang and regional expressions. If words are the tools, we need a large set for successful thought transfer.

Fluency is an important element here, too. We must be able to use all those tools and be especially skilled with the core tools we use the most. Think of a mechanic who has a tool chest filled with shiny new wrenches. The mechanic must know the purpose for each tool and how and when to use it. Fluency is a step beyond the "parrot response," where mention of a word triggers a rote definition that can be recited without fail—and without comprehension. Fluency means understanding a term so well that you will recognize its presence and meaning under any circumstance.

Literary fluency depends on mastering the specialized vocabularies of prose and poetry. Most of their terms are shared in a core vocabulary. Poetry uses more rhythm and rhyme terms than prose, perhaps, but a simile will be the same simile in either genre. Whether you are reading or writing, teaching or learning, working or relaxing, you will find it easier to communicate once

Premise *(continued)*

you master that core literary vocabulary. The examples, exercises, and explanations of this *Toolbook* are designed to go beyond a simple glossary and to bridge that vital gap between definition and mastery. It serves as a literary security blanket or safety net.

Quite probably you already know most of what is included here. But, when you are ready to share that great idea with the world, the tools in this book should give you the confidence of knowing that you will be understood.

Using These Tools

The premise that words are the tools we use to communicate is followed throughout *Toolbook*. All of the exercises are reality-based and constitute actual practice in using each new term as a tool. Since all of the pages may be reproduced, one method of presentation is to distribute a copy of all the pages, go over the explanation orally with the class, be sure they understand the instructions, have them complete the exercises, and go over their answers. Since this involves distributing quite a number of pages, on some of the terms you might prefer to give the explanation orally and distribute written copies of the exercises. With figures of speech, you may choose to distribute only the cartoon page, or only the cartoon and exercise pages. Challenge the students to find another example and draw (Yes, you may color it!) their own cartoon. Post the "winners" on the bulletin board.

Flexibility is a planned part of the book's construction. The book is geared to the student so you can pick and choose what you want to use. You, however, know your students, their requirements and abilities better than anyone else. The function of each lesson will vary with each grade level, with each individual class section, and with each teacher. Only you can assess how best to help your students reach that comfort level with these tools that is necessary for easy use.

Use your own literature book: Examples accompany most of the terms in this *Toolbook*, but you may find more relevant examples in your own textbook. Locate an example or two in advance to get your students started and then let the students find others. Some students might benefit from a contest of some sort. Who, for example, can find the most metaphors on a single page of Crane's *Red Badge of Courage*? More advanced students might be challenged to defend their discoveries. When or why, for example, can a simile be called personification? How can the same example be both? Why have both terms? This type of defense is particularly useful to help them understand some of the subtle differences between terms. *Toolbook* is designed as a supplement to your literature book because the examples your students discover on their own in their own books will make the terms more germane to them.

Hints for teaching poetry: Many speech problems stem from poor listening habits. Because rhyme is pleasing to the ear, students are inclined to listen more carefully to the exact sound of rhyming words. Pairs of words that rhyme are more easily remembered than pairs of words that do not. A student who has difficulty reading aloud may be encouraged to memorize and repeat a poem aloud. In addition, some accent problems can be corrected by pairing the mispronounced word with a "sound alike" word.

Faulty rhythm also causes pronunciation problems. Listen carefully to speech that is difficult to understand. Quite often the trouble comes from placing the accent on the wrong syllable. Learning how to "read" accent marking properly, or putting a troublesome word in a proper rhythm pattern will be helpful in correcting this.

(continued)

Using These Tools *(continued)*

Both rhyme and rhythm can be a great help for ESL students.

Correlate tool use with other subjects: Teachers often encounter the question "What good will this ever do me?" Showing these students a direct benefit that they might gain can go a long way toward helping them master these terms. One good tactic is to seek ways for them to use their new tools to help them in other subjects. Some examples of this are found in the section on Didactic poetry, but others are there to be tapped and implemented. Find out what problems they are having and show them how to invent learning helpers. Some examples of this might be:

Alliteration—Biology Suppose students are having a problem keeping separate the functions of phloem and xylem in a tree trunk. Suggest using alliteration—"Through the phloem flows the food."

Rhythm—Chemistry Remembering the rules for naming acids can be confusing. Sulphur<u>ic</u> Acid is Hydrogen Sulph<u>ate</u> and Sulfur<u>ous</u> Acid is Hydrogen Sulph<u>ite</u>. Use anapestic tetrameter and create an unforgettable slogan—

ˇ	ˇ	/		ˇ	ˇ	/		ˇ	ˇ	/		ˇ	ˇ	/
We	will	**ic**		if	we	**ate**		but	with	**ous**		it's	all	**ite.**

Acrostic—Earth Science Suppose students are having a problem learning the names of the planets in order from the sun outward. Suggest using an acrostic sentence:

<u>M</u>y <u>V</u>ery <u>E</u>arnest <u>M</u>other <u>J</u>ust <u>S</u>ails <u>U</u>nder <u>N</u>ew <u>P</u>lanets.

<u>M</u>y	<u>M</u>ercury
<u>V</u>ery	<u>V</u>enus
<u>E</u>arnest	<u>E</u>arth
<u>M</u>other	<u>M</u>ars (Mother is Ma)
<u>J</u>ust	<u>J</u>upiter
<u>S</u>ails	<u>S</u>aturn
<u>U</u>nder	<u>U</u>ranus
<u>N</u>ew	<u>N</u>eptune
<u>P</u>lanets	<u>P</u>luto

(If they include the Band of Asteroids, try <u>M</u>y <u>V</u>ery <u>E</u>arnest <u>M</u>other <u>A</u>lways <u>J</u>ust <u>S</u>ails <u>U</u>nder <u>N</u>ew <u>P</u>lanets.)

Part 1: Basic Tools

Senses

 Senses are the means through which we perceive our surroundings.

Imagine you are a radio. You can receive on only five stations. There may be thousands of stations sending out programs, but you have five and only five receiving stations, so you can only receive five programs. Your stations are **see**, **hear**, **taste**, **touch**, and **smell**. If you can't see it, or hear it, or taste it, or touch it, or smell it, then it does not exist for you.

Reception is not automatic. You have to have your set turned on and tuned in to receive anything at all. You can improve reception by fine-tuning the stations. If one station is impaired or missing, you can compensate by turning up the volume on other stations, but nothing will completely

Prose and Poetry

Name _____ Date _____

replace the missing signal. Actually, you are that radio and any concept you have of your universe is received through one or more of those five senses.

You and I may have the same five senses, but this does not mean we will always receive the same signals. Some of us may have trained one sense more than another. For example, perhaps we see better than we hear. If all eyes were exactly alike none of us (or all of us) would need eyeglasses. None of us (or all of us) would be color-blind. Our transmission systems and brains vary as much as do our eyes. It is no wonder that two eyewitnesses to the same event seldom give the same account of what happened.

How would you describe color to a person who has been blind since birth? What descriptive terms would you use? Light and dark are of no value. Brightness and shades have no meaning for him.For someone who is blind, colors simply do not exist. He or she may be able to use other senses to replace some of the things a sighted person understands, such as how to feel certain shapes, but try describing a mountainside covered with aspen trees in full fall colors!

A writer needs to be aware that the more senses appealed to at the same time, the greater will be the possibility of accurate idea transfer. If a scene involves a scared boy, for example, don't simply say "He was scared." Did his hands feel cold and clammy? Did he hear advancing footsteps? Did he see shadowy monster shapes approaching? Did he taste the blood when he bit his lip in terror? Did he smell the musty, moldy wall he shrank against?

Now, can you add anything to "He was scared" that will let your reader better sense the fear? If you don't reach your readers on one sense channel, maybe you will get through on another, so appeal to as many as

possible. Successful writers understand and use combined sense involvement. References may be very subtle and still be very effective. Notice how skillfully Thornton Wilder evokes all five senses in this brief excerpt from his play *Our Town:*

(Just after her death near the end of the play, Emily has been granted her wish to relive a day from her life. When her chosen day begins, however, she reacts as someone with a shiny new bicycle might view an outgrown tricycle, something to remember fondly but no longer needed. She ends her visit abruptly and, as she turns to go back, she says good-bye to those life things that were once so vital to her, things she will remember fondly, but no longer needs.)

EMILY: . . . So all that was going on and we never noticed. Take me back— up the hill—to my grave. But first: Wait! One more look.—Good-bye, Good-bye, world, Good-bye, Grover's Corners—Mama and Papa—Good-bye to clocks ticking —and Mama's sunflowers. And food and coffee. And new-ironed dresses and hot baths . . .

Did you realize that in this simple speech she recognized each of her five senses?

Good-bye to clocks ticking (*Hear* the clock tick)—**and Mama's sunflowers** (*See* the yellow blooms). **And food** (*Taste*) **and coffee** (*Smell* the aroma). **And new-ironed dresses and hot baths** (*Feel* the smooth cloth and the warm water) . . .

To paraphrase Emily, *was all that going on and I never noticed?* It is not necessary to name the individual senses, but readers should be aware of the need to activate all five senses to understand the author's full thought or idea. Just because we can hear, for example, doesn't mean that we always listen. All of us, at one time or another, have become so engrossed in one thing that we

Name _____ Date _____

have tuned out everything else. *Having* all five senses and *using* all five are separate things. To comprehend the complete message of the author, we need to be sure that all our senses are alert and working when we read.

 Exercise 1.1

Read the following sentences and decide which "sense channel" the author was appealing to:

1. The church bell bonged its deep call to evening . . . . _____
2. The cold draft pulled at her as she crept up to the fire . . . . _____
3. The sweetness of the syrup was nauseating to . . . . _____
4. The mountain purpled in the distance . . . . _____
5. Her rough calluses scraped on the silky . . . . _____
6. Orange blossoms wafted their welcome from . . . . _____
7. The frogs croaked their greetings across the . . . . _____
8. The shadows danced and swayed on the ceiling of . . . . _____
9. The pungent smoke enveloped him as . . . . _____

(1. hear, 2. touch, 3. taste, 4. see, 5. touch, 6. smell, 7. hear, 8. see, 9. smell)

Name _____   Date _____

 Exercise 1.2

Pick one of the situations below (or one you like better) and give a stimulus that might be used to trigger each of the five senses. Then pick two words a writer might use to describe the situation. Possible situations: Shipwrecked on a deserted isle, a concert for your favorite recording star, a football game.

Example	**Situation**—a birthday party
	Tasting Stimulus: Cake is served
	Tasting Response: (a) Chocolate (b) Sweet

Situation:

Tasting Stimulus:		
Tasting Response:	(a)	(b)

Touching Stimulus:		
Tasting Response:	(a)	(b)

Hearing Stimulus:		
Tasting Response:	(a)	(b)

Seeing Stimulus:		
Tasting Response:	(a)	(b)

Smelling Stimulus:		
Tasting Response:	(a)	(b)

Name _____   Date _____

Person

 Person identifies the pronoun voice used in a work. First (I) and second (You) person are informal or personal voices, while third (They) person is a formal or impersonal voice.

> Now **Person** comes in One, Two, Three
> And Number One belongs to **ME!**
> And **I** and **WE** and **OURS** and **MINE**
> Can help **US** Number One define.
>
> When **Person** shifts to Number Two
> Then I directly talk to **YOU**
>
> All the rest are Number Three
> Like **IT** and **THEY** and **HE** and **SHE.**

First person refers to one's self and is recognized by singular pronouns *I, me, myself, my, mine,* and plural pronouns *we, our,* and *us.* Any pronoun that indicates one's self, or any group to which one's self belongs, is the first person. *I* is used in the most personal types of communication, such as diaries and monologues. *I* will always be a part of groups such as "we" and "our."

Second person refers to the person spoken to directly and is recognized by the singular and plural *you.* It directly addresses another person. You also use the second person if the subject is understood to be "you," as in imperative commands such as "Come here!" "You" can be either singular or plural, but it always requires at least two people—the person (or persons) spoken to and the speaker. This is because I am the first person and if I speak to you, then you are the second person there, so you are the **second person**.

In **third person** both the speaker and the person spoken to are unidentified. Third person is recognized by the use of such indefinite singular pronouns as *it, he, she, her, his,* and *him,* and indefinite plural pronouns like *they, them,* and *their.* Since he or she is not I, and not you, then they will be the **third person**.

Indefinite pronouns, by their very nature, can cause problems for writers so they should be used very carefully.

Suppose Paco and Joe and Kim are sitting in class and the bell rings. Using indefinite pronouns, I might write "He put his book in his backpack." Now who put whose book in which backpack? Did Paco put Paco's book in Paco's backpack? Or did Paco play a joke on someone by putting Joe's book in Kim's backpack? Since third person uses indefinite pronouns, always be careful to make sure the identity is clear. Always remember: We're number one!

Name _____   Date _____

 Exercise 1.3

Using the numbers 1, 2, and 3, assign person to each of the following:

(a) _____ yourself   (j) _____ their

(b) _____ she   (k) _____ mine

(c) _____ I   (l) _____ you're

(d) _____ they   (m) _____ his

(e) _____ you   (n) _____ ours

(f) _____ her   (o) _____ himself

(g) _____ we   (p) _____ they

(h) _____ themselves   (q) _____ ourselves

(i) _____ myself   (r) _____ he

((a) 2, (b) 3, (c) 1, (d) 3, (e) 4, (f) 3, (g) 1, (h) 3, (i) 1, (j) 3, (k) 1, (l) 2, (m) 3, (n) 1, (o) 3, (p) 3, (q) 1, (r) 3)

Exercise 1.4

For each situation described, write one phrase or sentence in each of the three person voices that might be used to describe the scene or event.

Example	**Scene:** A person "cuts" into a long line of waiting people.
	First Person: I was so angry.
	Second Person: You were so angry.
	Third Person: He was so angry.

1.

Scene: A car runs out of gas on a lonely road.
First Person:
Second Person:
Third Person:

2.

Scene: A sale at (pick any store).
First Person:
Second Person:
Third Person:

Name _____   Date _____

Mood

Mood is the emotional tone in a piece of writing.

We learn at an early age what a direct effect **mood** has on results. We remember The Little Train who said, "I think I can, I think I can, I think I can!" The Little Train *believed* he could because of his determined mood and it led to his success.

Imagine that you need to get special permission from your mother to meet some friends at the mall tomorrow. You hurry home from school to ask, but find that Mom is very unhappy. While she was buying groceries, someone backed into her new car in the parking lot and dented the fender. Aren't you going to wait until she is in a better mood to ask about going to the mall? If her mood affects what she is able to understand, isn't it also possible that your mood affects what you are able to understand when you read?

Suppose two students of equal ability are assigned to read the same difficult, technical passage and report on it. Student A is apprehensive. He always gets the tough assignments. The teacher doesn't like him. The course is boring. He won't ever use this junk, so there really isn't much point in learning it. He knows before he starts that he won't understand it. Does Student A have any chance of completing this assignment successfully? Student B, also, is apprehensive. This is a tough assignment and she is really going to have to concentrate—maybe even read it twice. The only way to finish is to start, so. . . . What are Student B's chances? Assuming that the students have some measure of control over their moods, which one has the best chance to finish the assignment? As a reader you need to be aware of the influence that mood can have on your understanding of the material.

In the example about going to the mall, you were told that Mom was not happy. Usually, mood is determined more indirectly. When you read, look for clues in the types of words used or a character's action. Did he shout or murmur when he spoke? Did she throw the book or turn the pages gently? When you are looking for the mood of a character, look at his or her actions.

Sometimes the mood of an entire event will be more important than the mood of a single character. Now you may need another type of clue to find the mood. The weather is a favorite device of authors to indicate mood. Was it a stormy or a sunny day? Animals are another common tool used by authors to set the mood for an entire scene. As a character approached the field, did the cow stand quietly and chew its cud or did it paw the ground and lunge at the gate? Be alert to all types of mood clues.

It is often more difficult to name a mood than it is to be aware of or to feel it. To make naming a mood easier, try starting with broad terms like "good or bad" and "happy or sad." Once you have a general idea, try to narrow it down to something a little more exact. "Content" is more specific than "happy" for example, and "lonesome" is more specific than "sad." One way to be more exact is to look for the cause of the mood. "Vengeful" and "jealous" are more exact than "mad."

Even when you cannot give it an exact name, remember that awareness of mood is more important than what it is called. Just as the author is obligated to establish the mood, the reader is obliged to recognize the significant effect that mood has on understanding the author's intent.

Prose and Poetry

Name _____   Date _____

Exercise 1.5

Find a mood word for the following examples. Be as specific as possible.

1. The sneer is gone from Casey's lips
   His teeth are clenched in hate
   He pounds with cruel vengeance
   His bat upon the plate.

   —from "Casey At Bat"
   by Ernest Lawrence Thayer

   Mood _____

2. Nick snuggled under the blanket, holding sleep at bay so his thoughts could go back through their first week in the new town. The moving men were still unloading the van when their neighbor came across the yard with his arms full of puppies. Just like that, Nick had a new wiggly brown puppy named Buster and a brand new best friend living right next door named Cleve. Tomorrow . . . Buster's stubby tail beat a steady tattoo on Nick's pillows as slumber seeped in and dreams replaced memories.

   Mood _____

Name _____   Date _____

 Exercise 1.6

Look at the examples below. Imagine you are the author. What could you have each character do to illustrate the indicated mood?

Example	**Mood:** Happy
	Three-year-old boy: clap hands and run across yard laughing
	Adolescent girl: turn on radio and dance around room
	Grandparent: hum and smile while reading letter over and over

1.

Mood: Impatient or Worried
Three-year-old boy:
Adolescent girl:
Grandparent:

2.

Mood: Afraid or Scared
Three-year-old boy:
Adolescent girl:
Grandparent:

Name _____   Date _____

Plot

The plot is the plan of the events in a story, or the actions taken by the characters in a setting.

Understanding what is **plot** and what is not is "a piece of cake." To bake a cake, the steps would be (1) decide on what kind to bake, (2) gather and check all the ingredients, (3) use a pan the right size and pour in the mixed batter, and (4) let the oven heat change it from batter to cake. We can follow this same formula to understand the parts of a story.

(1) Decide on what kind of story to write. Is it a short story, a novel, science fiction, mystery, or romance?

(2) Gather and check all the characters in the story. Who are the heroes? Who are the villains? Are they suitable for this story?

(3) Select a time and place for the characters and story type you have selected. Is this a fitting setting for your kind of story and characters?

(4) Decide what actions the characters will take in this setting. The actions you plan are your **plot**. How will these actions cause your characters to change?

The change from batter to cake does not happen in an instant. We know that the batter changes while it is in the oven, but the change does not happen in a single moment. It takes the entire cooking time to produce the right results. The same thing is true of a story plot.

The plot is the sum of **all** the action in a story. Plot includes elements like the climax or turning point in the story. Plot also includes the events leading up to the climax (the rising action) and events following the climax (the falling action).

Which events to include and the sequence of those events are the two main decisions every plot planner must make. A longer story, such as a novel, allows greater freedom in event selection. The shorter the story, the more crucial it becomes to select only those activities that move the characters to their desired end point. Sequence does not present too great a problem when there are only a few events.

Sequence is a greater concern for the novelist. With more events included, the order of action is more complicated. The action should move logically and smoothly from one event to the next. There are times when an author will use a **flashback** to fill in some missing detail from the past. These remembered events should not be used too often, however, or they will interfere with the flow of the story.

Good plots have two main requirements: (1) content where the essential events are included and (2) sequence where events flow smoothly and make sense.

Name _____ Date _____

Conflict

Conflict is the opposition between two forces in a story.

Conflict is a basic element of the plot. It is usually identified as one of four types: (1) person versus person, (2) person versus nature, (3) person versus society, or (4) person versus self. Many plots will have more than one of these conflicts, but one will usually dominate the story.

One force, usually the main character, is called the **protagonist**. For there to be a conflict, something must oppose the protagonist. This opposing force is called the **antagonist**. If the antagonist wins the conflict, the work is called a tragedy. There is not a single term for those plots where the protagonist is the winner. Comedy is often used, but comedy implies humor. It is quite possible for the protagonist to win without the level of humor needed for comedy. *A Christmas Carol* by Charles Dickens is an example of this type of plot. Scrooge changes his ways and the story has a "happy" ending, but it does not rise to the level of humor required to call it comedy.

Person versus Person is a conflict or contest usually between two people. Person vs. person plots focus on such topics as a detective seeking the criminal or rivals fighting for either a promotion or a love interest. *The Adventures Of Sherlock Holmes* by Sir Arthur Conan Doyle or "The Murders in the Rue Morgue" by Edgar Allan Poe are examples of this type of conflict.

Person versus Nature is a contest between the protagonist and the environment. Jack London is commonly regarded as the best known author of works featuring this type of conflict. His Alaskan tales all contain some elements of this struggle, none better, perhaps, than his short story "To Build A Fire." Ernest Hemingway's *The Old Man and The Sea* is another example of this person versus nature theme.

Person versus Society is a struggle involving social issues such as class, race, or social order. War and politics are also popular topics. *Native Son* by James Baldwin or *Uncle Tom's Cabin* by Harriet Beecher Stowe exemplify this type of conflict.

Person versus Self is a conflict that centers around an inner struggle between the protagonist and his or her feelings. In Shakespeare's *Hamlet,* Hamlet struggles with himself throughout Shakespeare's play. In *Hamlet* this person versus self struggle is featured, but the play offers an example of another type of conflict: person versus person as Hamlet (the protagonist) struggles with his uncle (the antagonist).

 Exercise 1.7

Read each of the following paragraphs and decide what type of conflict it represents. Then name the protagonist and the antagonist.

1. Before the sun was up, Pete had been on the path to the woods right behind Uncle Frank and Cousin Lee. This was the first year the men had thought Pete was old enough to tag along and he proudly mirrored every move they made. They said the turkeys were huge this year and they were set on a great holiday feast. Uncle Frank and Lee had gone to their separate hunting areas and Pete waited now with his gun raised and ready in the spot

(continued)

Prose and Poetry

Name _____ Date _____

they had assigned to him. While he waited, he thought about the turkey family he had seen last summer. He had stumbled on Mama Turkey teaching two of her chicks to scratch for food. He wondered if one of those babies was big enough yet to make the main course for a big meal. Probably not. They were such little balls of fluff. The barrel of his gun began to dip. He remembered how Mama Turkey had talked to her babies, scolding and praising. Just like his mama talked to him. Suppose one of them was big now. Suppose one walked into his cleared spot. Would he be able to . . . ?

What type of conflict is this story based on?

Person versus _____

Who is the protagonist? _____ Antagonist? _____

2. The thirst that waked Millie was raw and so intense it had color and sound. She couldn't remember when it wasn't there. But something was different. What had happened? Slowly and through the fog of pain she realized she was no longer tossing on the churning sea, but lying on a sandy beach in the broiling sun. She would open her eyes soon, but for now she would just lie there and try to realize she was safe at last. Safe? Not without liquid on her parched tongue and throat. None of the small islands in the area had a water source. But there were palm trees. Maybe she could find a coconut tree. How would she get a coconut down? If she got it down, how would she break it open. She would just lie very still and think. When she opened her eyes, maybe she would . . .

What type of conflict is this story based on?

Person versus _____

Who is the protagonist? _____ Antagonist? _____

3. While he waited for Jack's interview to finish, Robbie stepped back and sat on the long bench. The secretary had said he would be next. Would he be able to make it through the interview? He knew he had to prove he deserved the promotion. He saw his reflection in the glass above the panel and tried to force a confident smile. Did that look confident or silly? No matter. He was too nervous to keep the smile. Jack had won every time they had fought since grade school. He remembered all the bruises Jack had embedded on his body and on his ego. *Not this time, Jack. Not this time, Old Buddy.* He thought about how Jack's face would look when he found out Robbie was the new foreman and the smile came unbidden. *Look out, Jack. It's my turn!* The secretary called his name and Robbie stood . . .

On what type of conflict is this story based?

Person versus _____

Who is the protagonist? _____ Antagonist? _____

Name _____   Date _____

Style

 Style is the author's manner of expression. It can be any element or combination of elements making the writings of an author recognizable.

Think of someone very close to you, someone you would recognize and pick out instantly across a crowded room. What is there that makes that person so easy to identify? Height? Weight? The way she moves? Her manner of speech? It may be that you can't give a name to the thing that makes you so sure you can single out that person. Call it her style. You just recognize her **style**.

When you read a poem with no punctuation, you might guess that it was written by e.e. cummings because that is his style. O. Henry is recognized by his surprise endings. Stephen Crane is noted for his use of metaphors, Willa Cather for her exact attention to botanical details, and Tom Clancy for his lengthy setting before the story begins. These are all style markers. The indicators range from punctuation to language to story structure, but they still do not cover all the things that can be used to pinpoint an author's style. There is no magic formula for what elements to look for to identify the style of an author; but style is there, distinctive and recognizable.

Imagine that Jack, your favorite professional sports star, has a young fan named Willy. On game day, Willy dresses in Jack's jersey and runs out on the field claiming to be Jack, the star. Wouldn't we know, immediately, that an impostor was on the field? In fact, wouldn't it be a little foolish for Willy to think we would believe he is Jack just because he is wearing Jack's jersey? Willy is not a professional athlete and he doesn't have Jack's style. Students are not polished, professional writers, nor are they expected to be. It is a mistake to imitate or borrow too much from the style of another writer. A student who attempts to "borrow" and to claim as his or her own a sentence or a paragraph from another source is just as foolish as Willy was. Not only is it plagiarism, but the shift in style will be obvious.

Your writing has a style. It may be the way you use verbs or the type of verbs you use or it may have nothing at all to do with verbs. It is yours, however, and it can be recognized. No idea has merit until it has been transferred, intact, to someone else. You have good ideas and they deserve the best explanation you can give them. Check your grammar and spelling because this will increase the ability of others to understand you, but use your own words to express your thought. If you produced the idea, only you can produce the explanation, so do it with your own style.

Name _____ Date _____

Theme

The theme is the general conclusion about human behavior drawn by a work. In some nonfiction, theme may be the general subject of the work.

The **theme** explains the author's purpose in writing a story. One of the best questions to ask when trying to find the theme in a work is, "What is this writer trying to prove?" When you have answered this question, you will have the theme.

Suppose you have a book about the Earl E. Burd family. They lived near Farmersville during the early 1900's. They rose before dawn each day and worked very hard. They were trying to pay for their new farm. Just before they made the last payment, they all got very sick and died, so the banker got their farm. Bad plot aside, what is it that the author is *trying* to prove in this story? (*"The Earl E. Burds got the germ"* will not work!) The theme must be *general*, so it will not use specific character or place names. A general statement could be "This book is about a farm family." Do we have a theme yet? No, we have something general, but we don't have a conclusion about human behavior yet.

We need to look for some kind of behavior conclusion in the book. The people in the Earl E. Burd family certainly did work hard. They tried to pay their debts. So we can say, "This is about a hard working farm family who tried to pay their debts."

Do we have a theme yet? No, we have a general statement about human behavior, but we need the conclusion drawn about this by the author. Is it good or bad to be a hard working farm family? Our author seems to think it is bad, but we don't agree with that. So we might state, "The author mistakenly decides that it is futile to be a hard working farm family."

Do we have a theme yet? No. We have to give the *author's* purpose. We do not have to agree with the author but we do have to give his or her conclusion if we are to have a theme statement. "It is futile to be a hard working farm family." We finally have a theme statement. It is general. It concerns human behavior. It gives the author's conclusion. We may not agree with it and there may be better ways to state it, but it fulfills our definition requirements and it is a theme statement.

Some nonfiction works will not fit this formula. If the purpose of the author is just to give a variety of details on a subject, the theme will simply identify the main topic. "This is a book about dog training" could be a theme statement for a nonfiction book about dogs and their training.

Name _____   Date _____

Point of View

 Point of view is the set of eyes the author uses to let the reader see the action unfold.

One way to understand **point of view** is to imagine a board that is solid white on one side and solid red on the other side. Observer A is on the white side and Observer B is on the red side. If the board is described as white, then we are hearing A's Point of View. If it is described as red, then we are hearing B's Point of View. If it is described as white on one side and red on the other, you are seeing both sides. Then the point of view is *omniscient,* which means all-seeing, or seeing all points of view.

Here's another way to think of it. Imagine you are in charge of televising a football game. You may have several different cameras placed around the football field. At any one time, one camera would be showing the game from its angle, or, from one point of view. Since the cameras are in different places, no two cameras will provide exactly the same picture. Each camera records a different image, or a different point of view.

If you are the director, you will decide which camera will give the audience the best view of a play on the field. The author, in like manner, decides which character's view will give the reader the best account of the story.

The author needs to decide on the point of view quite early in the writing process. He or she must be sure to report accurately what would be seen from there and be sure to keep the same point of view all the way through the story. Just as the author tries to view the action accurately from a particular angle, the reader must try to see it through the eyes selected by the author. The reader will never understand what the author is describing until he or she looks at it from the point of view selected by the author. This does not mean that the reader has to agree with the position of the author. Learning to distinguish between seeing a different viewpoint and agreeing with that viewpoint is essential to the discriminating reader.

Name _____   Date _____

To see the difference in the ways an author's point of view can be transmitted, consider the following scene: Mama Bird hurries back with food for her two hungry Baby Chicks whose nest is in the branches of Oak Tree. Moo Cow is grazing in the field near Alfalfa Plant and Cloud floats overhead.

 Exercise 1.8

Look at the drawing and think about each character's point of view. (The cast of characters includes: Mama Bird (MB), Baby Chicks (BC), Oak Tree (OT), Moo Cow (MC), Alfalfa Plant (AP), and Floating Cloud (FC).) Then read each of the statements below and write down the name of the character who would most likely make each of the following statements.

1. Help! I'm next and I don't want to be eaten! _____

2. Drat it all! How would you like a messy nest in your hair? _____

3. Where is Mama? She sure is taking her sweet time! _____

4. What a peaceful scene! Everyone looks so happy down there. _____

5. Why is the alfalfa so much greener in that other field? _____

6. Ungrateful kids! All they do is complain and all I do is work! _____

(1. AP, 2. OT, 3. BC, 4. FC, 5. MC, 6. MB)

Prose and Poetry

Name _____ Date _____

Slant

Slant has two different forms, both concerned with the choice of facts or language. <u>Reader-based</u> slant affects the language and facts included as they are influenced by the age, the ability, or the interest of the intended reader. In <u>author-based</u> slant, the author attempts to promote a specific position or "side" of a subject and this affects both the selection of facts and the way emphasis is given to them.

All authors do a certain amount of "slanting" when they write because it is impossible to include absolutely everything connected to an event. Suppose you are writing to tell what happened last night when your uncle came for a visit after his trip to Scotland. How long was his trip? How much did it cost? What was his hotel like? What did he eat on his trip? Did he bring you a present? How old is he? How many times did his heart beat during the visit? How fast was he breathing? How many molecules of air were in the room? How many did he inhale? If you think some of these things are trivial and not important, fine, but remember that you have just made a decision about what was important and that you chose what to include or omit. When fact or word choice is made for some purpose other than this type of necessary selection, we call it **slant**.

Reader-based slant is usually evident by its content and language. The terms that would be used to explain a subject to a three-year-old would differ from those used to explain the same subject to a college student. Imagine that you are a writer for an age-specialized magazine (kindergarten children, for example) and you have been assigned to write an article about the development of a new cure for a dread disease. Young readers may be interested in very little beyond how it will taste or if a hypodermic needle is involved. An older child, on the other hand, may want to know a little more about it. This child might

wonder how long the cure lasts, if it will make her sick, and how it will taste or if a hypodermic needle is involved. Adults might want to know how much the cure will cost, where they have to go to get it, who discovered it, how much money the discoverer will make, what the possible side effects are, how long the cure lasts, how it will taste or if a hypodermic needle is involved. Research scientists will have an entirely different set of interests. The wise writer will slant the writing to interest the particular audience. Reader-based slant is based on the interests, abilities, or requirements of the reader.

Author-based slant is used by an author to present a particular position in its most favorable light. It is a method of persuasion. A writer uses writer-based slant to favor a certain position at the expense of an opposing view. Most political speeches and advertising are examples of writer-based slant.

Consider the case of Kitty K. You have just interviewed her for a job and it is your duty to decide whether or not your firm will hire her. You must be able to support your recommendation with reasons. All of the facts in the following list are true:

- Kitty K. is 18 years old and is of average height, weight, and appearance.

- She is the oldest of four children.

- Her mother, a single parent, was injured severely in a car accident three years ago and died last year of those injuries.

- Kitty was alto soloist in the school choir. In her junior year she won first place in state solo choir competition, but later dropped out.

- She was caught by police on curfew violation last year (claimed she had been working).

- She was on the honor roll regularly, as are all her siblings.

- She dropped out of school last year, six months before her expected graduation.

- She has had two jobs previous to this, and quit both jobs.

- She refuses to work the night shift.

If you decide **to hire** her, your recommendation might say:

She is a bright, unselfish person who accepts challenges. She postponed her own education and career plans to help take care of her mother. She assumed full responsibility for her younger siblings following her mother's death. She will need a permanent day-shift assignment because she feels she must be at home with her siblings at night.

If you decide **not to hire** her, your recommendation might say:

She is not the type of person on whom we can depend. She is a school dropout with a police record. She can't keep a job because she is very uncooperative and refuses to accept alternate shift assignments. She quit the school choir even though she knew they were depending on her for upcoming state competition. She never finishes what she starts.

Both statements have a basis in the facts given. The difference is in the facts selected and the manner in which they were presented. Both are examples of writer-based slant.

Name _____   Date _____

 Exercise 1.9

Now you try your hand at **reader-based slant**. Make up your own list of "facts" for a new cereal. How much does it cost? How does it taste? What is its nutrition value? Can you get coupons? Is there a toy included? Does a famous person endorse it? Then write a one-line ad for each of the three age-specialized magazines listed below. Use the "facts" you have created to write the ads.

Facts: _____

_____

_____

1. Kids' Kapers Magazine _____

_____

2. College Events Magazine _____

_____

3. Golden Oldie Notes _____

_____

 Exercise 1.10

Now put **writer-based slant** to work for yourself. Read the following pairs of statements. Both are true and refer to the same bicycle. Assume that you want to sell that bicycle. Put an X by the statement you would choose to include in an ad to help you get the best price.

1. _____ a. The frame is beginning to rust.

   _____ b. Will paint to suit new owner.

2. _____ a. The spokes are in excellent condition.

   _____ b. New tires are needed.

3. _____ a. It has new brakes.

   _____ b. Poor brake design causes frequent replacement.

4. _____ a. It is 15 years old.

   _____ b. It has reliable 15 year record.

5. _____ a. It has a new padded seat.

   _____ b. The original seat wore out.

(1. b, 2. a, 3. a, 4. b, 5. a)

If you used the other statement from each pair, do you think you could get as much money for your bicycle?

Name _____ Date _____

Setting

Setting, as it is used in literature, is the time and place of the action.

HOUSTON,... UH, WE HAVE A PROBLEM!...

In **setting**, the **time** refers to the general period of the plot, not to the time that passes within the story. (For example, "this story took place in the Roaring Twenties," not "this story took place in a day and a half.") The **place** refers to the general or the main location, even though other sites might enter the story briefly. (For example,

"this story took place in New England," even if the story began while the *Mayflower* was at sea.) Time and place are equally important parts of the setting.

Setting is a "pair word" like *couple*. Pair words must have two parts. One person, alone, can never be a couple. Time, alone, or

Prose and Poetry

Name _____ Date _____

place, alone, can never be a setting. As the Wise Old Sage said about these pair words (if he didn't, he should have) "It takes two to make one." To quote another Wise Sage, "You can't have one without the other."

Setting is stated in the positive, always telling what it *is* rather than what it is *not*. It would be proper to say that it could be anytime, but it is not proper to ignore the time element or to say it does not have a time. The same positive approach applies to place. You may say that it could be anyplace, but you would not say that it has no place. Setting, then, is always stated as a positive and both time and place are always mentioned.

When describing the setting of a work, general terms are usually acceptable. Using *The Grapes of Wrath* as an example, it could be said that this book is about an Oklahoma family migrating to California during the Great Depression. The time could be just as well identified as the early 1930's or during the Dust Bowl, but you must give something that identifies the general era. One element might be very specific, such as "March 4, 1931," and the other very general, such as "North America." The presence of both time and place are required, but there is no set requirement about generality.

Some authors make the setting quite obvious; sometimes it becomes an essential part of the work. At other times, when details are not given directly, you have to learn to look for clues. Notice, for example, how the characters travel or communicate. These elements will give you some idea of the general time. George Washington did not send any faxes to his troops nor did he

ride a Harley to the office. If a fax is sent in the work you are analyzing, it must be in modern times. Clothing and speech are also possible sources of setting clues, so if a character wears anything or says anything, check to see if some setting element is revealed. Did the characters have an unusual accent or use language associated with a specific region? Did someone wear a bikini or a fur coat? Climate and surroundings will yield place clues. Negatives can be as useful as positives—there are no oceans in Kansas, and Alaskan sand dunes are pretty scarce. Often, deciding where and when the story is *not* may lead to where and when the story is.

An author may eliminate all hints of time or place to emphasize that something can be found anywhere or anytime. Lyric poems of emotion are prime examples of this. Love poems, for example, can be structured so that they could apply to a Neanderthal cave dweller or to a creature of the future in outer space. This does not mean that they do not have a setting. In cases like this where the author seems to have left out both time and place on purpose, and you still have a blank on the line where you have to fill in the setting, do not despair. There is a solution. It may be said that the setting is universal, or that the work is set anytime and anyplace. If one element is present and the other appears to be missing, do not ignore the missing element. State it, for example, as being in the mountains of Virginia at an unknown time. Even when some universality is there, the setting can be stated as a positive.

Name _____ Date _____

Character

 Character is the identity of an individual. The total character has three areas, the <u>outer person</u>, the <u>social person</u>, and the <u>inner person</u>. All three of these areas are combined in the identity of each character, but they are separate and independent of one another.

The **outer person** is all of the physical characteristics of a person including age, sex, and stature. These physical features usually form our first picture of people we meet. Suppose you see a stranger commit a crime. What sort of thing could you tell the police so they could recognize the criminal on sight? Height? Weight? Sex? Clothing? Posture? All those things are part of the outer person, the physical identity of a character. As a general rule, whatever you can see is physical and is a part of the outer person. An author usually provides the physical descriptions of the outer person directly with statements like "She was a slender seven year old" or "Freckles covered his face and arms."

The **social person** shows the general and the personal relationships of the character to other people. This part of identity is called social because it requires a relationship between at least two people to exist. General social relationships will include things like occupation, financial standing, and community reputation. To understand why things like this require a second person, suppose we use financial standing. A person is "rich" or "poor" only in comparison to someone else. Suppose we measure wealth in carrots. Is a person with twenty carrots wealthy? To a person with one carrot, he is "rich," but to a person with a thousand carrots, he would be "poor." One cannot be a teacher without having a pupil, or a doctor without having a patient. All of these things establish the general relationship of a character to his society. Personal relationships will include things like family structure,

friendships, enemies, love relationships. A relationship with another individual is required for all of these personal identities to be valid. To be a parent requires having a child, to be an enemy requires having a foe. As with the outer person, authors usually identify the social person directly with statements like *He is a librarian*, or *She was an only child.*

The **inner person** reveals the emotional and moral composition of the character. Is the person honest? Quick-tempered? Happy? The author seldom makes a direct statement about this inner person, but usually gives the reader clues to make decisions about these characteristics. The character will return a wallet intact or hum a merry tune, for example, and the reader can decide on the inner-person qualities these actions disclose. This method of revelation is used in part because these identifications are often too complex to be reduced to a simple descriptive term. The action itself is simply a plot activity. The reason behind the action is what the reader needs to discover the inner person. Before you decide that the returned wallet means the character was honest, check the reason why it happened. Perhaps the wallet was found by a confidence man who sought to use its return to gain favor with a future victim. In this case, the return of the wallet is far from honest, so the action alone does not reveal the inner person. The reason behind the action must be taken into account to establish inner-person qualities.

Consider the action of a man jumping off a bridge. Until we know why he jumped,

Prose and Poetry

Name _____ Date _____

it is simply a plot activity. Was he escaping from the law? Was he trying to save a drowning child? Was he attempting suicide? Was he going for a swim on a hot day? Only when his reason for jumping is known will it disclose any of the inner person. These actions often are woven into the plot of the story. The other two areas are reasonably constant throughout the story, but the inner person may show evident change from the beginning to the end of the plot. This change may even *be* the plot.

It is important to have a thorough understanding of the reasons behind each of the three divisions of character. A first glance at *smart*, for example, might suggest that it is part of the inner person, but this is not correct. To be smart is physical because the brain is a part of the body. Is he wise? Only by knowing how and why this brain is being used will the inner person be revealed as wise or unwise.

 Exercise 1.11

Now see if you can identify the area for each characteristic below. Use <u>O</u> for <u>Outer</u>, <u>S</u> for <u>Social</u>, and <u>I</u> for <u>Inner</u> to determine the type of characteristic for each.

1_____Tall

2_____Wise

3_____Middle child of three

4_____Spoiled

5_____Stout

6_____Mother

7_____Generous

8_____Bald

9_____Student

10_____Red hair

11_____Wealthy

12_____Jealous

(1. O, 2. I, 3. S, 4. I, 5. O, 6. S, 7. I, 8. O, 9. S, 10. O, 11. S, 12. I)

Prose and Poetry

Name _____ Date _____

 Exercise 1.12

Below you will find a series of numbered sentences. Each sentence describes an action that might happen in a story.

First, pick a character trait that the action might suggest, such as kind or cruel, honest or dishonest, selfish or unselfish, etc. Next, write an explanation that gives the reason or reasons why this character's actions shows that trait.

Example	**Action:**	Sondra smiled as she picked up the twenty-dollar bill.
	Trait:	selfish
	Reason:	Sondra had seen the money fall out of a customer's wallet at the newsstand. She didn't know the person, so Sondra decided she could just keep the money for some CDs she wanted; it didn't really matter how she got the money.

1. **Action:** Rick laughed as he drove off.

   Trait: _____

   Reason: _____

2. **Action:** Risa turned quickly and walked away from the school.

   Trait: _____

   Reason: _____

3. **Action:** Denzel threw himself down on his bed.

   Trait: _____

   Reason: _____

 Exercise 1.13

Make up a paragraph about either Juanita or Jesse for your new novel. Reveal at least one characteristic in each of the three areas—the outer person, the social person, and the inner person. Invent whatever details you need.

_____

_____

_____

_____

Prose and Poetry

Part 2: Figures of Speech

Figures of Speech

Figures of speech such as similes and metaphors are some of the tools in a writer's store of devices. Most of them say what is not literally true in order to establish exactly what is intended.

That may sound confusing, but consider the student with a mountain of homework. Just how many pages of paper would it take to make even a small hill? Think of the girl who is pretty as a picture. Which wall do you plan to hang her on? Draw a picture of a girl with rosy cheeks, pearly teeth, and stars in her eyes. Did you draw in her thorns, oyster shells, and galaxies? As you can tell, figures of speech are not intended for literal translation. Since they can be so confusing, why use them? The answer is that they can create an "instant on" picture. It took Shakespeare an entire play to establish the romantic characteristics of Romeo, for example, but refer to someone as Romeo and you can produce in one word

what it took a literary master an entire play to achieve. **Figures of speech** can be real power tools for a writer.

See if you can recognize the difference between what is actually said and what is really meant by some of these—*died of embarrassment, a tower of strength, sharp as a tack,* or *buried her head.* None of these is literally true, but you understand their meaning. They are all figures of speech. Think of a figure of speech you have heard or used recently and draw a picture of it in the space below. Show it to someone else and see if they can guess your figure of speech. (If you can't think of one right away, feel free to borrow one of those already mentioned.)

Name _____   Date _____

Figures of speech are so common that, often, we are unaware they are present. Consider this situation:

A new college student oversleeps her first night in the dorm. She has to dress and get across campus in a hurry to try to make it to class on time.

Throw in a few figures of speech and this might become:

When she saw the clock, the green freshman realized she had pulled a Rip van Winkle. "Mamma Mia!" she said, "What a great way to start!" She hotfooted downstairs as gracefully as a hippo. Just a lamb among wolves, she strapped on her backpack like a knight strapping on armor. Her books weighed a ton and she was glad she had new roller blades. They had cost a pretty penny and they hummed as she crossed the campus at full speed because the rule book said it was important to be on time.

Can you find at least 12 different types of figures of speech in that paragraph? They are identified and explained to the right, but try to find them for yourself before you peek. Feel free to mark on the copy below:

When she saw the clock, the

green freshman realized she had

pulled a Rip van Winkle.

"Mamma Mia!" she said, "What

a great way to start!" She

hotfooted downstairs as

gracefully as a hippo. Just a lamb

among wolves, she strapped on

her backpack

like a knight strapping on armor.

Her books weighed a ton and she

was glad she had

new roller blades. They had cost

a pretty penny and they

hummed as she crossed the

campus at full speed because the

rule book said it was important

to be on time.

To identify those figures of speech used:

the green freshman—**metaphor**, because her color is not really green. She is simply acting in a naive way, as inexperienced as a new, fresh, green leaf or blade of grass.

Rip van Winkle—**literary allusion**, because referring to a fictional character created a picture. Since old Rip slept forty years, we assume the student overslept.

"Mamma Mia!"—**apostrophe**, because her mother is not present to respond. She is talking to someone (or something) that cannot respond.

"What a great way to start!"—**irony**, because she means it is not great at all. She said the opposite of what he meant, sarcastically.

hotfooted—**synecdoche**, because the whole girl went downstairs, not just her foot. The feet are the most affected part involved in running.

Name _____   Date _____

as gracefully as a hippo—**oxymoron**, because hippos are not at all graceful and are about the last thing one would associate with grace. It is accurate in that she was clumsy, and would be a simile if it were stated "as clumsy as a hippo."

a lamb among wolves—**antithesis**, placing opposites together to make the characteristics of each more dramatic. The helplessness would not be as noticed if she were a lamb with other lambs as when she is the only lamb among the wolves.

strapped on her backpack like a knight strapping on armor—**simile**, she is not really a knight but, "like" a knight, is prepared to face the dangers of the day with the same courage.

Her books weighed a ton—**hyperbole** (overstatement), because they may have weighed a pound or two, but a ton is an extreme exaggeration.

cost a pretty penny—**understatement**, because roller blades certainly cost more than a penny, a great deal more than even a bright, shiny, pretty penny.

they (roller blades) hummed—**personification**, because humming is a human activity. Skates cannot sing or hum, but their sound may resemble that human activity.

the rule book said—**metonymy**, because books cannot speak.

Prose and Poetry

Name _____   Date _____

It Figures

This rhyme was written to help teach
Some figures we use in our speech.
The dozen terms we will review
Are given here from A to U.

It seems a star shines twice as bright
That shines alone in darkest night.
To emphasize, **ANTITHESIS**
Puts opposites in pairs like this.

When you use an **APOSTROPHE**
You speak to someone absentee
"Oh, World!" "Oh, Death!"
     "Oh, Mountain High!"
How'll you feel if they reply?

If you would use **HYPERBOLE**
Exaggerate outrageously.
Let molehills into mountains grow
Or tears make oceans overflow.

Now when you speak in **IRONY**
A real sarcasm is the key.
If "honor" was what Brutus had
Then why did Caesar bleed so bad?

When we refer to Romeo,
Allude to Cupid with his bow.
We make our point without confusion
Because of **LITERARY ALLUSION**.

When two unlikes you match direct
A **METAPHOR** makes them connect.
The streams are snakes, toupees are rugs,
And human arms give big bear hugs.

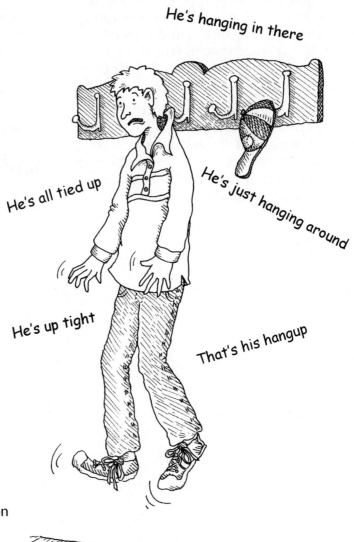

(continued)

Name _____   Date _____

METONYMY, now what this means
Is boiling pots instead of beans.
Or schools that issue rules and such
(Since bricks can't really talk that much!)

An **OXYMORON** grinds a gear.
An unexpected term you hear,
A mob that's screaming silently
Can have a riot quietly.

PERSONIFICATION is realized
When things not human are humanized.
This lets clouds skip on high and play
And trees lift leafy arms to pray.

You make a **SIMILE** distinct
When "LIKE" or "AS" two unlikes link.
Try she's as wrinkled AS a prune
Or her pride swelled LIKE a balloon.

A groom who seeks his fair bride's hand
Will want the whole gal, understand?
SYNECDOCHE gives us this twist,
Not amputation at the wrist.

The boy said, "Oh, that smarts a bit."
As on his thumb the hammer hit.
The **UNDERSTATEMENT** he did blurt
To let you know it REALLY HURT!

Now if this poem's helped explain
A bunch of terms that were a pain,
Then let me toss you one more term:
DIDACTIC poems help you learn.

—Helen Ruth Bass

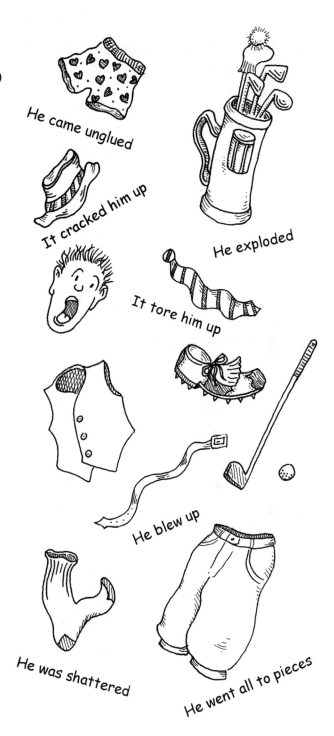

He came unglued

It cracked him up

He exploded

It tore him up

He blew up

He was shattered

He went all to pieces

Name _____   Date _____

Antithesis

Antithesis places opposites together to make the features of each seem more intense.

It seems a star shines twice as bright
That shines alone in darkest night.
To emphasize, ANTITHESIS
Puts opposites in pairs like this.

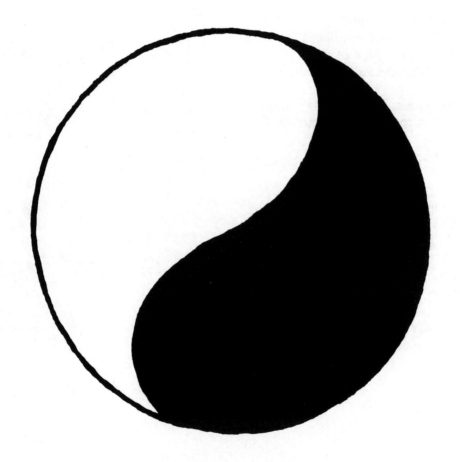

Antithesis

Name _____ Date _____

About Antithesis:

The purpose of **antithesis** is to heighten the details of an object. Suppose you want to draw attention to a drop of water. An effective way to make it distinct is to separate it from other drops of water. Place the drop of water in a dry spot and it takes on new values. So does the dry spot.

Antithesis is often used to hint at impending changes in the action. For example, if things are going to improve for a character, a single green shoot may appear in the snow as a harbinger of spring. Antithesis, in this case, the single splash of color in the winter white, is a metaphor that implies fortunes will improve for the character. You may notice the scene more because the green shoot contrasts so sharply with its surroundings. Antithesis is most effective when used sparingly, but it should not be overlooked as a composition device. An author can highlight a single characteristic by giving it a contrasting setting. The hero seems more honest when in the midst of thieves.

Examples (And why they are examples):

The light in the window was a beacon in the night. The light would not be seen in the daylight because there is not enough contrast. At night, however, the light seems brighter and the night seems darker because they are beside one another.

The flower bloomed brazenly in the weed patch. The flower, that might not even be noticed in the midst of a flower bed, demands notice because it is alone in the weeds.

His scream of protest echoed through the empty corridor. The fact that he is alone makes his voice ring louder than it would seem if he were in the middle of a crowd of clamoring objectors.

Not an example (And why not):

The tree grew in the forest. We are not likely to see this particular tree in much detail because it is in the midst of so many others it matches. Think how much more attention would be paid to every part of the tree if it were alone in the middle of a desert.

Name _____ Date _____

 Exercise 2.1

For each of the following items, suggest an opposite or contrast that might be used to highlight it:

Example	Item	Opposite/Contrast
	sad	happy

	Item	Opposite/Contrast
1.	loud laughter	_____
2.	a rainstorm	_____
3.	a seedling	_____
4.	a baby	_____

 Exercise 2.2

Look at the following list of items. On line (a), pick either the entire item or something distinctive about each item to highlight, then on line (b), pick some type of contrast for the selection.

Example	a new toy
	(a) new doll with long golden curls
	(b) toy box full of bald or patchy-haired dolls

1. a kitten

   (a) _____

   (b) _____

2. a new dress

   (a) _____

   (b) _____

3. an athlete

   (a) _____

   (b) _____

Prose and Poetry

Name _____ Date _____

Apostrophe

Apostrophe is addressing someone or something that is absent, abstract, or inanimate.

When you use an APOSTROPHE
You speak to someone absentee
"Oh, World!" "Oh, Death!" "Oh, Mountain High!"
How'll you feel if they reply?

Prose and Poetry

Name _____ Date _____

About Apostrophe:

There are so many different types of figures of speech that we may tend to confuse some of them, but we have a way to make **apostrophe** easy to remember. In contractions, such as *can't, won't,* etc., the punctuation that replaces the missing or absent letters is an apostrophe. Speaking to something or someone that is missing or absent is also apostrophe. While we do not encounter someone talking to a bird very often in everyday life, it happens fairly often in both poetry and fiction. Entire novels can be built around getting a wall to tell its secrets. It may, however, be as brief as a simple, "Oh, Dear!" if "Dear" is not present. Once we recognize them, we realize that other forms of apostrophe are pretty common in everyday life. Did you ever talk to the TV set? How about the motorist who begs his car not to run out of gas or the person whose checkbook won't balance? Did you ever ask the rain to go away? Once you learn to recognize it, you realize apostrophe is pretty ordinary after all.

Examples (And why they are examples):

Hail to thee, blithe Spirit!
from "To a Skylark" by Percy Bysshe Shelley (Shelley talks to and praises the skylark through the entire poem, but no response is expected from the skylark.)

Thou, too, sail on, O Ship of State!
Sail on, O Union, strong and great!
from "The Building of the Ship" by Henry Wadsworth Longfellow (Longfellow refers metaphorically to the government as a ship, then speaks directly to the ship in this poem. He does not expect to hear an answer.)

Roll on, thou deep and dark blue Ocean, roll!
from "The Sea" by George Gordon, Lord Byron (This poem is sometimes listed as "Apostrophe to the Ocean.") As in the poems above, the poet speaks to the ocean through the entire poem, but he does not expect it to speak back to him.

Not an example (And why not):

"Dad, can I have the car tonight?" Bill asked his father. Not all conversation is apostrophe. Bill is speaking directly to his father and will receive an answer, even though it may not be the one he wants to hear.

Name _____ Date _____

 Exercise 2.3

Now, to prove you know enough about apostrophe invent some of your own:

(a) Select an item you can see from where you are now. (item)

(b) Think of a reason to speak to that item. (reason)

(c) What would you say? (speech)

Example	(a) item: clock
	(b) reason: I'm bored
	(c) speech: Come on, clock, move faster!

1. (a) item: _____

   (b) reason: _____

   (c) speech: _____

2. (a) item: _____

   (b) reason: _____

   (c) speech: _____

 Exercise 2.4

Select an imaginary item (something you can't see from where you are now) to talk to. Is it something you want to praise or blame for something? Do you want to ask questions? What conversation will you have? Write four questions or statements that could be made to that item.

1. Item: _____   2. Item: _____

   _____   _____

(a) _____   (a) _____

   _____   _____

(b) _____   (b) _____

   _____   _____

(c) _____   (c) _____

   _____   _____

(d) _____   (d) _____

Prose and Poetry

Name _____ Date _____

Hyperbole

Hyperbole is an extreme exaggeration. It is often called overstatement, but it must be an exaggerated overstatement.

If you would use HYPERBOLE
Exaggerate outrageously.
Let molehills into mountains grow
Or tears make oceans overflow.

They laughed their heads off . . .

Name _____   Date _____

About Hyperbole:

Hyperbole is a step beyond mere exaggeration. It brings attention to some feature because it is so far beyond the realm of possibility that it is not intended to be taken at face value. Poetry, especially love poems, are a good source for finding hyperbole. Loving someone until all the seas run dry would be hyperbole, and Robert Burns promises to do that in "O, My Luve's Like a Red, Red Rose,":

> And I will luve thee still, my dear,
> Till a' the seas gang dry.

Advertising is another source of everyday hyperbole. Did you really expect to become an Olympic champion by eating a certain breakfast food? Will some new perfume or toothpaste really make all your wishes come true? This expansion of the limits is not confined to poetry and advertising. We read in prose of pioneers who "irrigated the land with the sweat of their brows." We even heard about a youngster wanting to go to a party who claimed that "everyone" would be there. Hyperbole often enters arguments, but seldom wins one.

Examples (And why they are examples):

Her boom box was loud enough to wake the dead. No amount of noise will quite do that! This is an extreme exaggeration.

I have a million errands to run today. If you run 100 errands a day every day, it would take over 27 years to run a million errands—

$100 \times 365 \times 27 = 985,500$—you still have 14,500 more errands to run in year 28, so this is an extreme exaggeration.

He hit the ball a country mile. Again, quite an extreme exaggeration.

Not an example (And why not):

I caught a trophy fish! (Actually, it was barely big enough to keep.) This is surely an exaggeration, but is just in the "stretcher" category. A minnow reported as a whale would be hyperbole.

Name _____ Date _____

Exercise 2.5

Find some element in each of the following situations and write your own hyperbole:

Example	A girl shopping: **Element:** how much she spent **Hyperbole:** she spent a million dollars in the first store (Element could have been how tired she was or how much fun she had or how long it took, etc.)

1. **Buying a new car:**
   Element: _____
   Hyperbole: _____

2. **Food in the cafeteria:**
   Element: _____
   Hyperbole: _____

3. **First day of school:**
   Element: _____
   Hyperbole: _____

4. **The first day of summer vacation:**
   Element: _____
   Hyperbole: _____

Exercise 2.6

Finish each of the following sentences with your favorite hyperbole:

1. That baby was _____

2. That test was _____

3. The track star was _____

Name ___Leila Lakhal___ Date _____

Irony

Irony, as a figure of speech, is mocking sarcasm that causes a statement to have the directly opposite meaning from what is said. (Irony can have a slightly different connotation in plots.) Other figures of speech are identified by the wording, but irony is usually identified by the circumstances under which the statement is made.

Now when you speak in IRONY
A real sarcasm is the key.
If "honor" was what Brutus had
Then why did Caesar bleed so bad?

Prose and Poetry

Name _____ Date _____

About Irony:

Irony can be found in many forms. Perhaps a blind person says, "I see what you mean," or a deaf person says, "I hear you wanted a job." It may be a nickname, such as "Shorty" for a very tall person, or it might be something like calling a very close election a "landslide." Because they are very brief and the intended meaning will not be found in a literal translation, all of these qualify as figures of speech. Irony also exists in more direct forms. It may be an obvious reversal or falsehood within a sentence, such as depicting the cruelty of war by asserting "War is kind," or it can be a short episode in a story, or it can be the focus of the entire plot. Episode or plot use occurs when a desired result is achieved, but the result is some form of disappointment or disaster. Another explanation might be "When you get the puppy you begged for, but it bites you." A classic example of this use of irony is found in the short story "The Monkey's Paw" by W. W. Jacobs. (A couple receives the exact amount of money they wished for, but it comes to them as a payment for their beloved son's death.) An example of irony in art might be a painting of a soldier's gun with a rose in the barrel. A mocking reversal is the common thread that runs through all types of irony.

[handwritten margin note: careful what you wish for.]

Examples (And why they are examples):

"I'm rich!" said the man with a dime. This is only irony because the man really means a dime is not much money.

"I'm so graceful!" said the girl when she tripped on the curb and fell down. This is irony because she really means she thinks falling down is clumsy.

"Great weather!" said the boy looking out the window at a rain storm. This is only irony because the boy does not like the weather at all.

Not an example (And why not):

"Great weather!" said the boy looking out the window at a beautiful day. This is not irony because the boy really does like the weather.

Name _____   Date _____

 Exercise 2.7

For each of the following statements, describe a circumstance where it would (a) be an example of irony and (b) not be an example of irony.

Example	"What a bummer!"
	(a) irony: I just won the big jackpot.
	(b) not irony: Someone just wrecked my new car.

1. **"That dress has style!"**
   (a) irony: _____
   (b) not irony: _____

2. **"I love that sound!"**
   (a) irony: _____
   (b) not irony: _____

3. **"I'm happy to meet you."**
   (a) irony: _____
   (b) not irony: _____

4. **"My date book is filled."**
   (a) irony: _____
   (b) not irony: _____

 Exercise 2.8

What expression of irony might you make in the following situations?

Example	a loud party: Great place for a nap!

1. getting grounded: _____
2. a boring speech: _____
3. a screaming baby: _____
4. a really hard test: _____

Name _____   Date _____

Literary Allusion

 Literary allusion is the creation of an instant identification by referring to a well-known person, place, or thing from literature.

When we refer to Romeo,
Allude to Cupid with his bow.
We make our point without confusion
Because of LITERARY ALLUSION.

Shop-Til-U-Drop Mall
Business Directory

Hercules Gymnasium

_____

Emperor Clothing Company

_____

Neptune Marine Supply

_____

**Noah & Sons
Shipbuilders**

_____

**Sawyer & Finn, Inc.
Painters**
Fences Our Specialty

_____

Midas Investment Company

_____

Hairstyles by Delilah

**King Arthur
Table Company**

_____

Dracula Tattoo Parlor
Body Piercing Specialists

_____

Gulliver's Travel Agency

_____

Sherlock Detective Agency
Cyclops Private Eyes
Pinocchio Lie Detectors

_____

Jack Spratt Diet Foods

_____

Mother Hubbard's Pantry

_____

Godiva Riding Stables

Name _____ Date _____

About Literary Allusion:

Mythology is a rich source for subjects that create instant pictures. How could we ever have Valentine's Day without Cupid or his arrows? Such names as Apollo and Neptune are used by NASA. The winged foot of Mercury is almost automatically associated with florists, and the idea of swift delivery is obvious. Religious literature is another ready supply for allusions that are instantly recognized. Such places as Mecca and Eden are universal and do not require religious affiliation to be used. The comic strips supply Superman and other heroes. It is clear that literary references, or **literary allusions**, are not limited to novels, short stories, and poetry.

There need not be any confusion when actual history—rather than fictional literature—is the supplier of the allusion. Some authorities cite a technical difference between historical and literary allusions, but the writer need not be too concerned about whether Camelot is fiction or nonfiction to use the allusion. Instant identification is more of a factor than the source when selecting a subject for allusion. The movies and television are becoming sources, but caution should be used that the example is universally known when selecting an example because fads fade and examples can lose their meanings. It is no longer literary allusion if it must be explained.

Examples (And why they are examples):

My new boss should be named Scrooge. Reference to Scrooge tells the reader that the boss is a stingy miser because of the reference to the Dickens character in *A Christmas Carol*.

He felt the weight of the world on his shoulders. This refers to Atlas in mythology who held the world on his shoulders. Allusion does

not need to use the name of Atlas because the mythological feat is enough identity to be recognized.

Their cabin was a Shangri-la. A picture of a remote sanctuary is created because of the hidden kingdom in James Hilton's *Lost Horizon*.

Not an example (And why not):

He visited a gloomy castle. The castle creates a picture, perhaps, but it is not a specific reference to a castle in literature that is known for gloom.

Name _____   Date _____

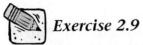 *Exercise 2.9*

Assume you want to emphasize the following elements. On line (a), think of a literary source that exemplifies each. Then on line (b), write a possible sentence you could use as an example.

	strength:
Example	(a) Hercules
	(b) He had the power of Hercules.

1. **weakness:**

    (a) _____

    (b) _____

2. **beauty:**

    (a) _____

    (b) _____

3. **anger:**

    (a) _____

    (b) _____

Exercise 2.10

For each of the following words or phrases, indicate on line (a) what emotion or feature is associated with the reference. Then on line (b), write a sentence that would show how the word or phrase might be used:

	a house of straw:
Example	(a) weakness
	(b) His plan collapsed like the first pig's house of straw.

1. **Tarzan:**

    (a) _____

    (b) _____

2. **Sherlock Holmes:**

    (a) _____

    (b) _____

Prose and Poetry

Metaphor

A metaphor is a direct comparison of two unlike things. Metaphors do not use <u>like</u> or <u>as</u> for comparison.

When two unlikes you match direct
A METAPHOR makes them connect.
The streams are snakes, toupees are rugs,
And human arms give big bear hugs.

"It's a jungle out there."

Name _____ Date _____

About Metaphors:

Both metaphors and similes are so common that many of them have become clichés and they are hardly recognized as figures of speech. The names chosen for sports teams, for example (bears, lions, falcons, etc.), are usually metaphors for strength, cunning, or attitude. Not too many teams are named for sparrows. Metaphorical car names usually emphasize speed or endurance, such as jaguars or mustangs. What other product names or slogans can you think of that are really **metaphors**?

Many other figures of speech are, basically, either metaphors or similes. Literary allusions use literature for one of the unlike objects, and personifications use humans for one of the unlike objects for examples, but both are basically either metaphors or similes. Metaphors may be made with almost any part of speech. In "the stream's a snake," a noun is used, and in expressing the same comparison with an adjective might be "the snakelike river twisted through the valley." A verb could be used for this comparison in "the river snaked through the valley." Just be sure not to use "like" or "as" because that turns the metaphor into a simile.

Examples (And why they are examples):

He hogged the road. Humans and animals are unlike things. He is not really a hog, but he has acted in a manner often attributed to hogs by taking more than his fair share of something.

She toyed with the idea. Her thought process is unlike a toy, but the implication is that she considered the idea so lightheartedly that it is as if she were playing with a toy.

Dad was a rock through all their trouble. Dad and a rock are unlike objects, but his ability to remain unchanged through pressure conditions is compared to a rock not being changed by the conditions around it.

Not an example (And why not):

Dad was a man through all their trouble. Dad is a man, so unlikes are not compared, even though being a male adult and acting like a man may imply different things.

Name _____   Date _____

 Exercise 2.11

When creating a metaphor, some element of the subject must be selected for comparison. If a meal is the subject, the element could be the way the food tastes, or the way the table looks, or the number of diners, or the table manners of the guests, but not until the element is singled out can something be chosen for picturesque comparison.

Look at the following words. Choose what element might be chosen from each of the following words for comparison.

Example	**campfire:** element—comfort (could have been safety, or smoke in your eyes, etc.)

1. **sunrise:**

   element: _____

2. **an owl:**

   element: _____

3. **a trumpet:**

   element: _____

 Exercise 2.12

What might you use to symbolize each of the following?

Example	**anger:** symbol—a storm

freedom:

symbol: _____

neatness:

symbol: _____

Pick any pair from above and create your own metaphor. **Remember not to use "like" or "as."**

_____

_____

Prose and Poetry

Name _____ Date _____

Metonymy

Metonymy is using a word closely associated with the one intended.

METONYMY, now what this means
Is boiling pots instead of beans.
Or schools that issue rules and such
(Since bricks can't really talk that much!)

The office had a party . . .

Name _____ Date _____

About Metonymy:

Metonymy is often called the sneaky figure of speech because the association between the two terms is so close that we seldom notice the wrong term has been used. Learning to notice them may be the best way to explain them. How many of the following have you heard without realizing an associated term had been slipped in for the intended term?

We will have the fatal wreck for you on the noon newscast! They will have the story about the wreck, not the wreck itself.

The bench ruled on the criminal's punishment. The judge ruled from the bench, but benches can't issue rulings.

The jockey galloped to a win. Surely the horse did the galloping.

The army said he was too old. How many people had to agree and speak at one time?

The book said Eli Whitney was an inventor. Maybe he invented a book that could talk?

Examples (And why they are examples):

I'm out of gas. If you really mean this at a service station, open your mouth for the hose! You probably mean your car is out of gas.

His rear axle broke. Did it hurt? Did he go to the emergency room?

Mother warmed the rolls. How hot did she get them? Don't you imagine the oven had more to do with the heating than Mom?

Not an example (And why not):

Mother punished me. Some mothers have a real talent for this. The right one to give punishment is named, punishment is the intended activity, and the correct recipient is named, so there is no metonymy here.

Name _____ Date _____

 Exercise 2.13

Examine the examples of metonymy below. Decide on line (a) WHAT makes each metonymy. On line (b), decide WHY each example is metonymy.

	Jill flew to Chicago.
Example	(a) what—Jill flew
	(b) why—Jill has no wings and can't fly.

1. **I knew as soon as I heard the shot that Billy had hit the deer.**
   (a) what: _____
   (b) why: _____

2. **Jane has a flat.**
   (a) what: _____
   (b) why: _____

3. **The radio said it would rain.**
   (a) what: _____
   (b) why: _____

 Exercise 2.14

Use each of the following so that you create your own metonymy.

	a hotel:
Example	I asked the hotel to send up some fresh towels.

1. **the Pentagon:**

   _____

   _____

2. **the White House:**

   _____

   _____

3. **the Olympics:**

   _____

   _____

Prose and Poetry

Name _____ Date _____

Oxymoron

An oxymoron is the use of a totally unexpected or unmatched term to create an intended impression. Unlike most figures of speech, an oxymoron states exactly the literal meaning.

An OXYMORON grinds a gear
An unexpected term you hear,
A mob that's screaming silently
Can have a riot quietly.

He was eighty years young.

Name _____   Date _____

About Oxymoron:

With metonymy, the substituted term is slipped in unobtrusively. With an **oxymoron**, the idea pairing attempts to grab attention. Consider a "perennial beginner." Normally, an activity is begun only once. This person makes so little progress that every attempt to participate is like the very first one all over again. The phrase might also suit a person who frequently starts new projects, but never finishes anything.

Have you ever heard someone argue a cause with false logic? Here's an example:

"Elephants like peanuts. I like peanuts. Therefore, I am an elephant." We might label the argument as "sensibly absurd." Because this says exactly what we mean and because these two words are not a natural pair, this is an oxymoron. When someone is asked to pay for a "free" prize (if there is payment, it isn't free), or a group rehearses for a "spontaneous" event (rehearsal eliminates spontaneity), the stage is set for an oxymoron.

Examples (And why they are examples):

Billy hurried to school at a crawl. If you ask Billy, he will assure you that he is going as fast as he can—"I'm hurrying!"—but he just doesn't seem to make very rapid progress, so his "hurry" is pretty slow—more of a crawl. Hurry and crawl do not match.

It was a banquet of one calorie. The picture on the box and the advertising will tell you it is a large serving, but there will not be much to chew on if it only has one calorie.

He was a dead-broke millionaire. This fellow has many things, most of them not paid for. He appears wealthy, but has no money. Broke and millionaire do not match.

Not an example (And why not):

He was a rich millionaire. We expect millionaires to be rich, so there is no unexpected term here.

Name _____ Date _____

 Exercise 2.15

Since oxymorons use opposite terms in combination, think of an opposite for each of the following terms.

Example	stately: opposite—sloppy

1. **open:**

   opposite— _____

2. **alert:**

   opposite— _____

3. **bored:**

   opposite— _____

 Exercise 2.16

For each of the following situations, finish the statement to create your own oxymoron.

Example	The weatherman promised rain, but none came. The next day he said, "It was a <u>dry</u> thunderstorm."

1. A boy tried to shine his boots, but they were too scuffed to polish. They may have looked worse after all his work.

   After polishing for an hour, he achieved a _____ shine.

2. The girl had a room filled with trash, but to her each item was a meaningful memento. Her mother was coming for a visit, so she put it all in organized heaps.

   Her room was filled with clutter, but it was _____ clutter.

3. The man was always quoting authorities and stating endless facts. We had reason to doubt the authenticity and reliability of some of his shared knowledge.

   He had many _____ facts.

(Hint list for blanks. Use only as needed. Yours are probably better!)

closed	interested
dull	neat
fictional	sleepy

Name _____ Date _____

Personification

Personification is giving human characteristics that they did not possess to non-human things.

PERSONIFICATION is realized
When things not human are humanized.
This lets clouds skip on high and play
And trees lift leafy arms to pray.

The stars winked . . .

Name _____ Date _____

About Personification:

Personification is found in all types of literature. It is human nature to assign our own characteristics to other things. It leads a reader to identify with a subject more closely, so it becomes a valuable tool for any writer. "Trees" by Joyce Kilmer is often recognized as a classic example of the personification of a tree. Part of it is:

A tree that looks at God all day,
And lifts her leafy arms to pray;
A tree that may in Summer wear
A nest of robins in her hair;

It is quite easy to identify with some of the human characteristics he assigns to the tree. The branches become leafy arms that reach upward as if in prayer. The idea of birds building nests in our hair is a little more difficult to accept.

Examples (And why they are examples):

The stream crooned its lilting lullaby. While the sound made by the stream may help a person sleep, the stream cannot sing. Singing, in this case crooning, is a human activity that has been assigned to the stream.

The sun was eaten by the storm clouds. Eating is a human activity. Clouds cannot eat.

Mickey Mouse. Real mice do not wear clothes, speak in bubbles, or organize clubs. There are many examples of animals that have been given human qualities in fiction, such as Winnie the Pooh, Lion King, or Bambi.

Not an example (And why not):

The flower grew. While growing is a human activity, flowers and other living things also grow, so the flower is not doing something restricted to humans.

Name _____   Date _____

 Exercise 2.17

Personification is, probably, the easiest figure of speech to originate. For each of the following subjects, suggest a human attitude it might have or a human action it might take.

| **Example** | a new pair of shoes |
| | **human quality:** they pinch |

1. **a hurricane**

   human quality: _____

2. **a hot dog**

   human quality: _____

 Exercise 2.18

Now try your hand at more personification.

1. You are walking through a store and something begs you to buy it. What is it? Write a sentence using personification about this incident.

   _____

   _____

2. A child was hurt in a skating accident. He is now, finally, resting comfortably in his own bed. Write a sentence with personification that tells what the bed did to make him feel better.

   _____

   _____

3. A baby kitten is lost. A number of things are around it, but there is no sign of Mama Cat. Something nearby either frightens or soothes him. What is it? Write a sentence with personification that tells what happened next.

   _____

   _____

4. You just burned your tongue on hot chocolate. Give human qualities to the cup or to the chocolate and write a sentence with personification that tells what happened next.

   _____

   _____

Name _____   Date _____

Simile

 A simile uses (like) or (as) to compare two unlike objects.

You make a SIMILE distinct
When "LIKE" or "AS" two unlikes link.
Try she's as wrinkled AS a prune
Or her pride swelled LIKE a balloon.

Her eyes were like diamonds.

Name _____   Date _____

About Similes:

Similes have one great advantage over the other figures of speech—a magic trigger for identification. If it is a colorful or vivid description and the word *like* or the word *as* is there, it is almost certain to be a **simile**. Metaphors and others do not have this identity advantage. The fact that similes are used so often and recognized so easily serves to enhance rather than to lessen their value.

Similes and metaphors are the basis of most figures of speech. They are, usually, the first (and, sometimes, the only) imagery terms learned. Since they are so basic and prevalent, their purpose deserves emphasis.

The whole idea behind them is to create an instant picture that spotlights and clarifies the object. When the comparison must be explained, the instant recognition is doubtful. If the compared object is so complicated or so obscure that the immediate connection is lost, the intent is also lost. In these cases, the simile or metaphor becomes more a part of the plot than a figure of speech. As a figure of speech, a good rule is Keep It Simple. It can be very dramatic or colorful or absurd, but the comparison should be established in a flash.

Examples (And why they are examples):

He slept **like** *a log.* Boy and lumber are unlike things—compared with "like."

She was thin **as** *a rail.* Girl and rail are unlike things, compared with "as."

Granny was as blind **as** *a bat.* Granny and bat are unlike things—compared with "as."

The dog was as fast **as** *lightning.* Dog and lightning are unlike things—compared with "as."

Not an example (And why not):

He is as tall **as** *his brother.* Uses "as" for comparison, but he and his brother are both tall boys, so this does not compare unlike things.

Name _____ Date _____

Exercise 2.19

Similes are used so often that many of them are stale. You can finish many automatically:

Blind as a _____; Fat as a _____; Eats like a _____.

To construct your own simile, try a fresh approach. Think first: what are you describing? Pick an outstanding feature of the object to highlight. Find something **new** for comparison. She was as cold as _____ (ice has been done!) What can you think of that is cold that some-one else might not think of right away? Sort through your own experiences for some time or something you associate with cold. It does not have to be exotic. A bite of ice cream may cause a reader to get a better image of cold than a fly on top of Mount Everest. Try your hand at finishing some of these with something new:

1. As fast as _____

2. Smelled like _____

3. Hurt like_____

4. As fresh as _____

5. As busy as a _____

Exercise 2.20

A simile is often called a metaphor that uses *like* or *as*. Change each of the following expressions from a metaphor to a simile:

Example	**The treaty bridged the distance between the governments.** The treaty was like a bridge across the distance between the two governments.

1. The idea flamed inside her brain.

_____

_____

2. She washed the memory from her thoughts.

_____

_____

3. The painted desert was pretty.

_____

_____

Name _____ Date _____

Synecdoche

Synecdoche is using a part of something to represent the entire thing, usually the most affected (or the first) part.

A groom who seeks his fair bride's hand
Will want the whole gal, understand?
SYNECDOCHE gives us this twist,
Not amputation at the wrist.

The rancher added extra hands for the roundup.

Name _____   Date _____

About Synecdoche:

Some people avoid using this term because they are intimidated by the word itself. Both the pronunciation and definition are easier to remember if the NECK is emphasized while saying "suh - NECK - dough - key." Repeat this at least three times, aloud, concentrating on the NECK sound. A physical display of affection is sometimes called "necking," but more than just the neck is involved. Since a part is used to represent the whole, it fits our definition of **synecdoche**. So remember NECK as a clue to the pronunciation and to the meaning of the word. Practice saying synecdoche until it is easy to say.

Imagine the announcer who asks the audience to give the singer a hand, and say synecdoche three more times while the imaginary hands are thrown at the stage. If the Romans had not known a good synecdoche when they heard one, imagine what might have happened after Mark Anthony implored them to lend him their ears!

Examples (And why they are examples):

*She knew her **ABC's**.* She really knew the entire alphabet. A, B, and C are just the first letters of it.

*He **legged** it to town.* The whole boy went. Because he walked, his legs were the most affected part.

*He had new **wheels**.* He really had an entire car, not just the wheels, so the wheels—a part—represent the car—the whole.

*The **brain** is coming over to study tonight.* The brain implies intelligence, but, hopefully, an entire person will show up tonight. Unless the boy's brain is inside a full body, you might hesitate to open the door.

Not an example (And why not):

The glove was on his left hand. In this case, his whole body was not in the glove, so hand is just a simple part of his body. A mentioned part must refer to the entire body or thing to become synecdoche.

Name _____   Date _____

 Exercise 2.21

Read the following words or phrases. Use each of the following in two ways:
(a) as a synecdoche and (b) intended as a simple part.

	Heart:
Example	(a) Synecdoche: He was all heart.
	(b) Part: His heart was beating.

1. Blue Collar

   (a) _____

   (b) _____

2. Gumshoe

   (a) _____

   (b) _____

Exercise 2.22

Answer the following questions:

1. Why would "a paper" be synecdoche for an entire research report?

   _____

   _____

2. Why would "a mouthpiece" be synecdoche for a lawyer?

   _____

   _____

3. Why would "the tube" be synecdoche for a TV set?

   _____

   _____

4. Why would "hard hat" be synecdoche for a construction worker?

   _____

   _____

5. Why would "striped shirt" be synecdoche for a referee?

   _____

   _____

Name _____   Date _____

Understatement
(Litotes)

Understatement is stating an extreme reduction of the evident value or amount.

The boy said, "Oh, that smarts a bit."
As on his thumb the hammer hit.
The UNDERSTATEMENT he did blurt
To let you know it REALLY HURT!

The politician had a word to say.

Name _____   Date _____

About Understatement (Litotes):

An effective way to focus attention on the value or amount of something is by deliberately and obviously assigning it the wrong worth. The reader's immediate reaction of, "Oh, that has to be wrong!" focuses attention much more sharply than if the correct amount is used. If the supplied amount is too high, it is called hyperbole or overstatement. If it is too small, it is called either understatement or **litotes** (LIE-tuh-teez). Both hyperbole and understatement are effective as attention getters.

The hyperbole may be more familiar, but the next time you want to draw attention to some mundane statistic, try using an understatement instead. How long, for instance, did it take to write that dreaded report? The hyperbole might be "a zillion hours," and the understatement might be "a second or three." How much did the boy outweigh the sparrow—tons and tons or an ounce or two? Did the song whisper or thunder from the boombox? How many freckles did the boy have on his cheek? How much did the broken arm hurt? How long did the baby cry? How many hours did the athlete train for the big event? Notice that all of these situations center on some factor that can be measured, which is the key. Answering these questions by overly enlarging the actual measurement will be hyperbole, and lowering it severely will be understatement.

Examples (And why they are examples):

Their new car cost a pretty penny. The new car cost so much more than a penny, even a shiny one, that this is an understatement.

The beach had a grain or two of sand. There are obviously so many millions of grains of sand on a beach that the amount is empha- sized by the "grain or two," so this is an obvious understatement.

Going through high school takes a day or two. Since it takes years to go through high school, this is an evident understatement.

Not an example (And why not):

Going through high school takes four years. This is a reasonably accurate statement, so there is no understatement here.

Exercise 2.23

Read the sentences below. Put a <u>U</u> next to each understatement and an <u>H</u> next to each hyperbole:

1. The blizzard was a tad cool. _____
2. It took her an eternity to apply the lipstick. _____
3. The Home Run King got a hit or two in his career. _____
4. The chef had cracked open at least one egg while learning to cook. _____
5. The movie lasted forever. _____

(1. U, 2. H, 3. U, 4. U, 5. H)

Exercise 2.24

Make up an understatement about the object of each hyperbole below:

| Example | **Hyperbole:** She is the greatest cook who ever lived. |
| | **Understatement:** She can make fair toast. |

1. Hyperbole: The pine tree had ten zillion needles.

   Understatement: _____

   _____

2. Hyperbole: I spent a fortune on tickets to the movie.

   Understatement: _____

   _____

3. Hyperbole: The baby cried nonstop until he was nine months old!

   Understatement: _____

   _____

Part 3: Poetry Tools

Melody

 Melody is the name given to the pleasing sounds in music or in poetry.

In music, **melody** is indicated by the position the notes are placed on the scale. They are given names based on those positions such as B, D, C, or G.

f   e   d   c   b   a   g   f

Repeated sounds in speech are pleasing to the ear and, in speech as well as in music, are called the **melody**. The positions in the words of poetry where the sounds are repeated are given the names **alliteration**, **assonance**, and **rhyme**.

Alliteration — Assonance — Rhyme

Alliteration occurs when a sound is repeated at the beginning of the words. The "tongue twisters" that even very small children enjoy are examples of alliteration. Peter Piper picks his pickled peppers and Sally sells her seashells. These repeated sounds of the initial consonants make alliteration appealing to the ear.

Alliteration:

__M__ elody   *begining*

__M__ emory

__M__ arked

Assonance occurs when a sound is repeated in the interior of words. It is much more subtle than Alliteration or Rhyme, and our ears are not as well trained to detect its presence. Quite often when we hear something that sounds pleasant but we don't detect an obvious reason, Assonance is present. It is, usually, a vowel-consonant combination.

Assonance:

M __EL__ ody   *middle*

Rep __EL__ ling

F __EL__ low

Rhyme occurs when a sound is repeated at the end of words. It is probably the most familiar to us of all the position terms.

Rhyme:

Mel __ODY__

Par __ODY__

Rhaps __ODY__

end

Prose and Poetry

Name **Leila** _____ Date _____

There are several types of rhyme. Counting the involved consecutive syllables from the end of the word back toward the beginning, we establish **single**, **double**, and **triple** rhyme.

Examples	go ing (single) com ing	go ing (double) blow ing	glow ing ly (triple) know ing ly

Imperfect rhyme occurs when the eye tells you a word should rhyme because it has the same ending, but the spoken words do not rhyme or sound alike.

Examples	st **ove** g **ive** r **ough** gl **ove** f **ive** thr **ough**	(Note how these word pairs end with same spelling, and appear to, but do not rhyme.)

Near rhyme occurs when the words almost rhyme, but the match is not exact, as the **line** and **time**, for example. The *ine* and *ime* do not quite rhyme, but sound almost alike.

Internal rhyme occurs when a word in the interior of the line rhymes with the word at the end of the line, or when two or more interior words rhyme.

Examples	Here we go to the **show** or We go and **show** our tickets

There is an order of preference in naming the melody elements. Look first for rhyme. If it is present, it is named first. If rhyme is not present and you still detect similarity of sound, look for alliteration. Only when both of these elements are absent do you look for assonance.

Only the first *letter* of the word is part of alliteration, *not the first syllable*. The two words *fundamental* and *Sunday* start with first syllables that sound alike—*fund-* and *Sund-*. Since the *F* and *S* do not have the same sound, however, this is not alliteration. Even though they sound alike, you can't say that *fund* and *Sund* rhyme since rhyme occurs only at the end of the word. Having eliminated rhyme and alliteration,

but still detecting the similarity of sound in "und," you'll discover that f*und*amental and S*und*ay, as a pair, constitute assonance.

Most of us probably have more experience creating rhyme and alliteration than creating assonance. To produce assonance, one technique is to start with words that rhyme and change the endings so they no longer rhyme. For example, *croon, June,* and *spoon* are rhyming words. Change the endings of *croon* and *spoon* to *crooning* and *spoonful*. Now the words no longer rhyme. There is no alliteration, but you can still detect repeated "*oon*" sounds in *crooning, June, spoonful*. These repeated sounds are assonance.

Name _____   Date _____

Onomatopoeia

Onomatopoeia occurs when the sound of the word gives the meaning of the word.

Examples of **onomatopoeia** are words such as *moan, buzz, whisper, meow, sizzle, hiss,* or *ping.* The words sound just like the sounds they make.

Edgar Allan Poe is considered the master of onomatopoeia in both his prose and his poetry. His poem "The Bells" is generally recognized as the greatest example of sustained onomatopoeia ever written. Each verse sounds like the type of bell it describes.

Read aloud these excerpts from Verse III of Edgar Allan Poe's "The Bells." Listen for the onomatopoeia.

Hear the loud alarum bells—
Brazen bells!
What a tale of terror, now their turbulency tells!
In the startled ear of night
How they scream out their affright!
Too much horrified to speak
They can only shriek, shriek
Out of tune, . . .
How they clang, and clash, and roar!
What a horror they outpour
On the bosom of the palpitating air!
Yet the ear it fully knows,
By the twanging,
And the clanging,
How the danger ebbs and flows;
Yet the ear distinctly tells,
In the jangling,
And the wrangling,
How the danger sinks and swells,
By the sinking or the swelling in the anger of the bells—
Of the bells—
Of the bells, bells, bells, bells,
Bells, bells, bells—
In the clamor and the clanging of the bells!

Prose and Poetry

Name _____ Date _____

Rhyme Scheme

 The rhyme scheme is a record of the pattern of end sounds for the lines of poetry in a stanza.

Rhyme scheme is always recorded in lowercase letters and never records the end sounds for longer than one verse. When a second stanza in the same poem is noted, it is regarded as a new pattern and will begin with the letter *a*. This rule is relaxed only in very rare situations, where a sound in one verse is used in the next, and this reuse is an integral part of the pattern. (See Terza Rima in Stanza Patterns for an example.)

The sound at the end of the first line is marked with the letter *a* and all other lines within that stanza that end with the same sound, rhyming words, are also marked with an *a*. When all of these *a* endings have been identified, the first unmarked line from the beginning is marked with a *b*, and all end words rhyming with it in that verse are also marked with a *b*. The next unmarked line will be *c*, and so on, alphabetically, to the end of the stanza.

Let's look at the first verse of "Casabianca" by Felicia D. Hemans. The first line is:

The boy stood on the burning deck_

The sound at the end of the line is **eck**, so it will be marked with an *a* and all succeeding lines in that verse with an **eck** sound are also marked with an *a*.

The boy stood on the burning deck	*a*
Whence all but him had fled	_
The flame that lit the battle's wreck	*a*
Shone round him o'er the dead	_

The next unmarked line is the second line and the end sound is **ed**, so it will be marked with a *b* and all rhyming end words in that verse will also be marked with a *b*. (**ead** in the last line rhymes).

The boy stood on the burning deck	*a*
Whence all but him had fled	*b*
The flame that lit the battle's wreck	*a*
Shone round him o'er the dead	*b*

The rhyme scheme for a verse is written as a single word in lower case italics. The rhyme scheme for this verse would be: *abab*.

Name _____   Date _____

 Exercise 3.1

Read the following verses aloud or to yourself. Listen for the end sounds and create a rhyme scheme for each verse. Then check your marks at the bottom of the page.

It takes a heap o' livin' in a house t' make it home _____
A heap o' sun and shadder, an' ye sometimes have t' roam _____
Afore ye really 'preciate the things ye lef' behind, _____
An' hunger fer 'em somehow, with 'em allus on yer mind. _____
It don't make any difference how rich ye get t' be, _____
How much yer chairs an' tables cost, how great yer luxury; _____
It ain't home t' ye, though it be the palace of a king, _____
Until somehow your soul is sort o'wrapped 'round everything. _____

—*from "Home" by Edgar A. Guest*

I wandered lonely as a cloud _____
That floats on high o'er vales and hills, _____
When all at once I saw a cloud— _____
A host of golden daffodils _____
Beside the lake, beneath the trees, _____
Fluttering and dancing in the breeze. _____

—*from "Daffodils" by William Wordsworth*

One night in late October, _____
When I was far from sober, _____
Returning with my load with manly pride, _____
My feet began to stutter, _____
So I lay down in the gutter _____
And a pig came near and lay down by my side; _____
Then a lady who was passing stopped to say, _____
"You can tell a man who boozes, _____
By the company he chooses," _____
And the pig got up and slowly walked away. _____

"Judged by the Company One Keeps" (Author unknown)

(The rhyme schemes are: "Home"—*aabbccdd*; "Daffodils"—*ababcc*; "Company"—*aabccbdeed*)

Name ______________________________ Date ________________

Rhythm

Rhythm is the beat and the pace of words in a piece of writing.

Prose is unlikely to have a regular pattern, but sometimes it does have a recognizable tempo. Poetry, other than free verse, has a rhythm called the metric pattern. Just like the beat in music, the accents of the syllables in the words fall at regular intervals. English is a composite of so many languages that rules for where the accents fall are not routine. This irregularity adds to the difficulty of learning English as a second language. Because some poetry has such a pronounced and predictable rhythm, it is often used to help students learn where the accents fall in speech.

Rhythm is established by using different tools. One device is the **foot**. There are different kinds of feet, each consisting of a number of stressed and/or unstressed syllables. Feet combine to make a line of poetry. Different types of feet produce different paces because the unaccented syllables only take half as long to say as the accented ones. As a result, the more unaccented syllables in a line, the more rapid the pace. A line containing anapestic, dactylic, or amphibrach feet has two light syllables for each heavy one and mimics the sound of horses at a gallop. These feet are more suitable for humor and adventure topics than for stately subjects.

Trochaic and iambic feet both have alternating heavy and light accents. Trochaic rhythm starts with a *heavy* accent followed by a *light* one. When you read a line of trochee, you can almost hear the muffled drums and the measured cadence of a funeral march, making it appropriate for a poem of grief. On the other hand, an iambic line starts with a light accent followed by a heavy accent and echoes the regular rise and fall of ocean waves. Iambic rhythm has a lighter sound and is the most commonly used rhythm pattern. Trochaic rhythm "climbs the hill" and iambic rhythm "tumbles down" the same hill.

The names and composition of these feet might seem difficult to learn, but four of these used most often will help you learn them if you pronounce them correctly and listen. A foot of iamb is a light accent, followed by a heavy one—de DUM—and is said in that way—(eye AMB). A foot of trochee is a heavy accent, followed by a light one—DUM de—(TRO key). Anapest is two light accents, followed by a heavy accent—de de DUM—·An uh PEST). A Dactyl foot is a heavy accent, followed by two light ones—DUM de de—(DACK til foot). Because these feet are used so often, practice saying them aloud, overemphasizing the heavy accents. Soon the pattern and sound of each will be automatic, until your memory "hears" your own voice say them.

The symbols used to represent the syllables are: a hook (˘) for the light *de* or unaccented syllables and a slash (/) for the heavy (DUM) or accented syllables. These marks are customarily placed above each syllable when marking meter. A longer, perpendicular line is sometimes used to separate the feet. A short line drawn under each syllable before the accents are marked helps insure that each syllable has been identified for marking. The chart that follows shows the composition of 10 poetry feet, emphasizing the 4 most commonly used. Read the feet names aloud until you are comfortable with each term.

Name _____   Date _____

Number of syllables per foot	Name	Accents (Accented, DUM) / (unaccented, de) ˘	Examples
2	Iambic	˘ / de DUM	˘ / to DAY, ˘ / a WAY
2	Trochaic	/ ˘ DUM de	/ ˘ COM ing, / ˘ BASE ball
3	Anapestic	˘ ˘ / de de DUM	˘ ˘ / un a WARE, ˘ ˘ / lem on ADE
3	Dactylic	/ ˘ ˘ DUM de de	/ ˘ ˘ VIC tor ies, / ˘ ˘ BEAU ti ful

Less Used

2	Spondee	//	2	Pyrrhic	˘˘
3	Tribach	///	3	Molossus	˘˘˘
3	Amphimacer	/˘/	3	Amphibrach	˘/˘

Once you establish the type of foot in a poem, you then need to count how many are in the line. The list below shows the terms that can be combined with the types of feet to name lines of poetry.

(Notice the pronunciation and STRESS the right syllables.)

1 foot	monometer	(mo NOM e ter)
2 feet	dimeter	(DIM e ter)
3 feet	trimeter	(TRIM e ter)
4 feet	tetrameter	(te TRAM e ter)
5 feet	pentameter	(pen TAM e ter)
6 feet	hexameter	(hex AM e ter)
7 feet	heptameter	(hep TAM e ter)
8 feet	octameter	(oc TAM e ter)
9 feet	nonameter	(no NAM e ter)

Again, the names might seem difficult, but they are easier to learn than might first be imagined. To begin with, the last half of each term is "meter," to measure, so that takes care of half of the words before we start! *Mono* means one—a *monologue* is one person talking—so *monometer* is one measured foot. When we cut something in two, we say it is dissected, so *di* is two, and *dimeter* is two feet. How many wheels on a tricycle? Three, so *tri* is three and *trimeter* is three feet. What is the name of that huge military building in Washington, the one with five sides? Pentagon! So *penta* is five

Prose and Poetry

Name _____   Date _____

and *pentameter* is five feet. How many singers in an octet? Eight, so *oct* is eight and *octameter* is eight feet. Nonameter is the only one that begins with an "n" like *nine*, so *nonameter* is nine feet. Some people get *six* and *seven*, *hex* and *hept* mixed up, but we won't because we know that *six* and *hex* both have an *x*, which leaves *hept* for *seven*.

What this means is that we just plain have to learn the last one: *tetra* is four and *tetrameter* is four feet. O.K. Tetra is four. Tetra is four. Tetra is four (enough?). *Tetrameter* is four feet and that is all of them. Look at the list and see how easy they are. Read them aloud until they both look and sound natural to you.

Inversion

Inversion happens if the beat should vary within a line of poetry, perhaps a trochaic foot within an iambic line. Sometimes the poet simply could not find an iambic word for that spot and hopes you will read the line kindly. More often, true

inversion is used for effect. The reader senses something important that the poet wants to emphasize by the shift in rhythm. It loses its effect if used too often and will result in poor rhythm and worse poetry.

Caesura

Caesura is a short pause that can take the place of an unaccented syllable in the line. It will show up in the cadence of spoken language. A caesura cannot be used for an accented syllable because the pause would be too long. It is normal speech pace to pause sometimes at a comma, and nearly always at the end of a sentence or a question. When this happens inside a line, it is called caesura. Read the following line (aloud, of course) and notice the natural pause at the end of the question. If this pause were not taken into account by the author, it would disrupt the rhythm.

˘ / ˘ / ˘ / ˘ /
Oh CAN'T you STAY ? STAY and PLAY.

When we look at a line of hooks and slashes, it helps to put a marker between the feet. This makes them easier to identify and to name. Look for the point where the pattern begins to repeat. The marked line shown in the first column is ˘ / ˘ / ˘ / ˘ /. It is a series of iambic feet (˘ /) and it is easier to count if we put a mark between feet like this:

˘ / | ˘ / | ˘ / | ˘ /

Now you can see that there are four feet of ˘ /. This is called iambic tetrameter.

Now you can put your tools to use for **marking time**. Iambic pentameter is basic to the sonnet and blank verse, and is a good place to start in learning to mark rhythm.

Look at the following line:

   It's Christmas Eve and there in splendor bright

This is a line of iambic pentameter which you can mark one step at a time. Begin by drawing a line under each syllable. (You should find 10 syllables because Christmas and splendor both have 2 syllables.)

Prose and Poetry

Name _____   Date _____

It's <u>Christ</u> <u>mas</u> <u>Eve</u> <u>and</u> <u>there</u> <u>in</u> <u>splen</u> <u>dor</u> <u>bright</u>.

Now that you have marked the 10 syllables, read the line aloud and listen for the heavy accents. Put a slash (also called a stress mark) over each heavy sound.

      /   /   /   /   /

It's <u>Christ</u> <u>mas</u> <u>Eve</u> <u>and</u> <u>there</u> <u>in</u> <u>splen</u> <u>dor</u> <u>bright</u>

Read the line again and emphasize the heavy syllables to be sure you have found all of them. (To check yourself, reverse the stress and read it aloud. Christ MAS does not sound at all right. CHRIST mas is better.) Once you are sure you have found and marked all the heavy syllables, put hooks over the remainder of your syllable marks. These will be your light syllables.

  ˘   /   ˘   /   ˘   / ˘   /   ˘   /

It's <u>Christ</u> <u>mas</u> <u>Eve</u> <u>and</u> <u>there</u> <u>in</u> <u>splen</u> <u>dor</u> <u>bright</u>

Now your line of marks looks like this: ˘ / ˘ / ˘ / ˘ / ˘ /. Find where the pattern begins to repeat itself and draw a line between the feet. ˘ / | ˘ / | ˘ / | ˘ / | ˘ /. We have five feet of ˘ /, so our line is called iambic pentameter. Remember the sequence—mark the syllables, find the heavies, mark the lights, divide the feet, name the line. See if you can mark and name the pattern for:

I think that I can mark the beat _____

I know that I can name the feet _____

This rhythm stuff is really neat! _____

(If you got three lines of iambic tetrameter, smile and take a bow!)

Name _____   Date _____

 Exercise 3.2

For each line, look for the point where the pattern begins to repeat itself. Draw a marker between the feet. Then write the name of the line.

Example	˘ / ˘ ˘ / ˘ ˘ / ˘ (˘ / ˘ | ˘ / ˘ | ˘ / ˘) amphibrach trimeter

(Use this chart to check your memory for the names of the feet)

˘ /   iambic   / /   spondee   ˘ ˘   pyrrhic
/ ˘   trochaic   / / /   tribach   ˘ ˘ ˘   molossus
˘ ˘ / anapestic   / ˘ /   amphimacer   ˘ / ˘   amphibrach
/ ˘ ˘ dactylic

1. ˘ ˘ / ˘ ˘ / ˘ ˘ / ˘ ˘ / _____

2. / ˘ / / ˘ / / ˘ / / ˘ / / ˘ / / ˘ / / ˘ / _____

3. / ˘ / ˘ / ˘ / ˘ / ˘ / ˘ / ˘ / ˘ _____

4. ˘ / ˘ / ˘ / ˘ / ˘ / ˘ / ˘ / ˘ / ˘ / _____

5. / ˘ ˘ / ˘ ˘ / ˘ ˘ / ˘ ˘ / ˘ ˘ _____

6. / ˘ / / ˘ / _____

7. ˘ / ˘ ˘ / ˘ ˘ / ˘ ˘ / ˘ ˘ / ˘ ˘ / ˘ _____

(1. anapestic tetrameter, 2. amphimacer heptameter, 3. trochaic octameter, 4. iambic nonameter, 5. dactylic pentameter, 6. amphimacer dimeter, 7. amphibrach hexameter)

 Exercise 3.3

From the ballad "Casabianca" by Felicia D. Hemans, mark and name the lines:

The boy stood on the burning deck _____

Whence all but him had fled _____

The flame that lit the battle's wreck _____

Shone round him o'er the dead. _____

(Lines 1 and 3 are iambic tetrameter and lines 2 and 4 are iambic trimeter.)

Prose and Poetry

Name _____   Date _____

Stanza Patterns

The stanza pattern, usually recognized by the number of lines, is one type of identification for individual poetry verses.

STANZAS		
Identity factors and requirements for some verses		
Lines	**Name**	**Rhythm and Rhyme Scheme**
2 lines	Couplet	any rhythm, any rhyme scheme
2 lines	Rhymed couplet	any rhythm, *aa*
2 lines	Heroic couplet	iambic pentameter, *aa*
3 lines	Triplet (or Tercet)	any rhythm, any rhyme scheme
3 lines	Terza rima	any rhythm, linked rhyme (*aba, bcb, cdc, etc.*)
4 lines	Quatrain	any rhythm, any rhyme scheme
4 lines	Folk ballad (sea)	1st and 3rd lines iambic tetrameter 2nd and 3rd lines iambic trimeter *abab* or *abcb*
4 lines	Ballad (horse)	1st and 3rd lines anapestic tetrameter 2nd and 4th lines anapestic trimeter *abab* or *abcb*
5 lines	Quintet	any rhythm, any rhyme scheme
5 lines	Limerick	1st, 2nd, and 5th lines: anapestic or amphibrach trimeter 3rd and 4th lines: anapestic dimeter *aabba*
6 lines	Sextet (or Sestet)	any rhythm, any rhyme scheme
7 lines	Rime royal	iambic pentameter, *ababbcc*
8 lines	Octave	any rhythm, any rhyme scheme
8 lines	Ottava rima	iambic pentameter, *abababcc*
9 lines	Spenserian stanza	first 8 lines: iambic pentameter 9th line: iambic hexameter *ababbcbcc*
14 lines	Italian sonnet	iambic pentameter, *abbaabbacdecde*
14 lines	Shakespearian sonnet	iambic pentameter, *ababcdcdefefgg*
any	Acrostic	any rhythm, any rhyme scheme (subject of poem spelled by reading down across first letter in each line)
any	Blank verse	iambic pentameter, no rhyme
any	Free verse	no rhythm or rhyme requirements

Prose and Poetry

Stanza Pattern Examples

Some **stanza pattern** names are general terms and others are more specific. *Couplet,* for example, may be a general term used for any two consecutive lines of poetry, or it may refer specifically to a two-line stanza. A quatrain may be any four consecutive lines, or *quatrain* may refer specifically to an individual four-line stanza. Other stanza pattern names are more specific. A *sonnet* is always a single verse composed of fourteen lines of iambic pentameter with additional rhyme scheme and content requirements. The four-teen lines in a single sonnet, however, may be said to have three quatrains and a couplet or an octave and a sestet.

Although line count is an important factor for most stanza identifications, some verses have additional rhyme, rhythm, or content requirements. A few types of patterns, such as blank verse or acrostic poetry, may have any number of lines in a verse because they follow separate guide-lines.

Rhymed couplet

There are two kinds of people on earth today
Just two kinds of people, no more I say.

Not the good and the bad, for 'tis well understood
The good are half bad and the bad are half good.

—*from "Lifting and Leaning" by Ella Wheeler Wilcox*

Heroic couplet

Although each couplet has two lines, multiple heroic couplets may be combined in optional stanza patterns that have a variety of lines per verse—aabbccddee, etc. of iambic pentameter for any even number of lines per verse. With "closed" couplets, the though is complete with each pair of lines, but with "open" couplets this is not required. Identified by its rhyme scheme and rhythm, this pattern may have any number of line pairs per verse.

Know then, thyself, presume not God to scan,
The proper study of mankind is man,
Placed on this isthmus of a middle state
A being darkly wise and rudely great:
With too much knowledge for the skeptic side,
With too much weakness for the stoic's pride
He hangs between; in doubt to act, or rest;
In doubt to deem himself a god, or beast;

—*from "An Essay on Man" by Alexander Pope*

Prose and Poetry

Name _____   Date _____

Tercet

Here you come with your old music, and here's all the good it brings,
What, they lived once thus at Venice where the merchants were the kings,
Where St. Mark's is, where the Doges used to wed the sea with rings?

—*from "A Toccata of Galuppi's" by Robert Browning*

Terza Rima

Rhyme scheme marking should start anew with each verse, but the "linking" is shown as *aba—bcb—cdc—ded,* etc.

She must a little touch it; like the one lame
She walked away from Gauwaine, with her head
Still lifted up; and on her cheek of flame

The tears dried quick; she stopped at last and said:
"O knights and lords, it seems but little skill
To talk of well-known things past now and dead.

"God wot I ought to say, I have done ill,
And pray you all forgiveness heartily!
Because you must be right, such great lords; still . . ."

—*from "The Defense of Guenevere" by William Morris*

Quatrain

When the stars threw down their spears,
And watered heaven with their tears,
Did he smile his work to see?
Did he who made the lamb make thee?

—*from "The Tiger" by William Blake*

Quintet

East side, west side, all around the town,
The tots sang "Ring-a-rosie," "London Bridge Is Falling Down";
Boys and girls together, me and Mamie Rorke
Tripped the light fantastic
On the sidewalks of New York.

—*from "The Sidewalks of New York" by Charles B. Lawlor and James B. Blake*

Name _____   Date _____

Sestet

With aching hands and bleeding feet
We dig and heap, lay stone on stone;
We bear the burden and the heat
Of the long day, and wish 'twere done.
   Not till the hours of light return,
   All we have built we discern.

—*from "Morality" by Matthew Arnold*

Octave

Half a league, half a league
Half a league, onward.
All in the valley of Death
   Rode the six hundred.
"Forward the Light Brigade!
Charge for the guns!" he said.
Into the valley of Death
   Rode the six hundred.

—*from "The Charge of the Light Brigade"*
   by Alfred, Lord Tennyson

Less used are the **rime royal, ottava rima,** and **Spenserian stanza.** Examples of **ballad, limerick, sonnet, acrostic, blank verse,** and **free verse** are found in the Types of Poems section.

Name _____ Date _____

Types of Poetry

Poetry is distinguished from prose by a very thin line.

Normally, prose is recognized by its paragraph structure and **poetry** by its stanza, rhyme, or rhythm patterns. Free verse has no rhyme scheme or stanza pattern. Only by accepting that some latitude is permitted may various distinctions about poetry types be used. Perhaps the best definition of poetry is "not prose."

The first broad division of poetry is **narrative** and **lyric**. Since a narrator is someone who tells a story, it is easy to remember that narrative poetry tells a story. The main element of this type of verse is the plot that unfolds. It is comparable to the novel or short story in prose. Lyric poetry is more akin to the feature article, with more emphasis on the revelation of a character, a mood, a scene, or a variety of other topics. Many lyric poems are suitable for setting to music, but this type of poetry takes so many forms that the two most practical definitions for lyric poetry may be "not narrative," or simply "everything else."

The reviewer and the writer both need to have some understanding of the types of poems beyond the narrative–lyric broad division. Some of these subtypes are discussed in this section, but this is only a partial list of the more common terms. They often overlap, yet there is something distinctive enough to set each apart for recognition. A sonnet, for example, has some very exacting requirements that distinguish it from any other type of poetry. A poem that has met these requirements and is deemed to be a sonnet, however, may also be (a) acrostic, or (b) satirical, or (c) a parody, or (d) any, and/or all, and/or none of the above! Understanding the overlapping possibilities only emphasizes the necessity for comprehending the individual properties of each type.

The **epic** is a book-length narrative poem about a single hero or a group of people. Homer's *Iliad* and Longfellow's *Evangeline* are examples of epics. Because of their length, no examples are included here, but examples of most of the other sub-types are given. Many of these poems were written long ago and it is this factor that causes many young poets to believe that they should use terms like "methinks," "thou art," and "could'st" in order to qualify as poets. Many of the classical poems contain these terms only because they were in common usage when those poems were written. To keep the budding poet from becoming a blooming idiot, it should be remembered that this language is no more appropriate for modern poetry than it is for modern speech. The same rule applies to language choice that applies to all good writing:

Stick to what you know.

Name _____   Date _____

Narrative Poetry

Narrative poetry, one of the broad divisions of poetry, tells (narrates) a story. Narrative poems include epics and ballads and these are usually longer than lyric poems.

Casey at the Bat

It looked extremely rocky for the Boston nine that day;
The score stood two to four, with but an inning left to play,
So, when Cooney died at second, and Burrows did the same,
A pallor wreathed the features of the patrons of the game.

A straggling few got up to go, leaving there the rest,
With that hope which springs eternal within the human breast.
For they thought: "If only Casey could get a whack at that,"
They'd put even money now, with Casey at the bat.

But Flynn preceded Casey, and likewise so did Blake,
And the former was a pudd'n, and the latter was a fake.
So on that stricken multitude a deathlike silence sat;
For there seemed but little chance of Casey's getting to the bat.

But Flynn let drive a "single," to the wonderment of all,
And the much-despised Blakey "tore the cover off the ball."
And when the dust had lifted, and they saw what had occurred,
There was Blakey safe at second, and Flynn a-huggin' third.

Then from the gladdened multitude went up a joyous yell—
It rumbled in the mountain tops, it rattled in the dell;
It struck upon the hillside and rebounded on the flat;
For Casey, mighty Casey, was advancing to the bat.

There was ease in Casey's manner as he stepped into his place,
There was pride in Casey's bearing and a smile on Casey's face;
And when responding to the cheers he lightly doffed his hat,
No stranger in the crowd could doubt 'twas Casey at the bat.

(continued)

Prose and Poetry

Name _____ Date _____

Ten thousand eyes were on him as he rubbed his hands with dirt,
Five thousand tongues applauded when he wiped them on his shirt;
Then when the writhing pitcher ground the ball into his hip,
Defiance glanced in Casey's eye, a sneer curled Casey's lip.

And now the leather-covered sphere came hurtling through the air,
And Casey stood a-watching it in haughty grandeur there.
Close by the sturdy batsman the ball unheeded sped;
"That ain't my style," said Casey. "Strike one," the umpire said.

From the benches, black with people, there went up a muffled roar,
Like the beating of the storm waves on the stern and distant shore.
"Kill him! Kill the umpire!" shouted someone on the stand;
And it's likely they'd have killed him had not Casey raised his hand.

With a smile of Christian charity great Casey's visage shone;
He stilled the rising tumult, he made the game go on;
He signaled to the pitcher, and once more the spheroid flew
But Casey still ignored it, and the umpire said, "Strike two."

"Fraud!" cried the maddened thousands, and the echo answered "Fraud!"
But one scornful look from Casey and the audience was awed;
They saw his face grow stern and cold, they saw his muscles strain,
And they knew that Casey wouldn't let the ball go by again.

The sneer is gone from Casey's lips, his teeth are clenched in hate,
He pounds with cruel vengence his bat upon the plate
And now the pitcher holds the ball, and now he lets it go,
And now the air is shattered by the force of Casey's blow.

Oh, somewhere in this favored land the sun is shining bright,
The band is playing somewhere, and somewhere hearts are light;
And somewhere men are laughing, and somewhere children shout,
But there is no joy in Boston: Mighty Casey has struck out.

—Ernest Lawrence Thayer

Prose and Poetry

Name _____   Date _____

Lyric Poetry

Lyric poetry is one of the broad divisions of poetry. It is based on a single thought or emotion. It includes a wide variety of patterns including elegies, Haiku, didactic, acrostic, and epigrams.

Rudyard Kipling was quite outspoken on many of the social issues of his time. His views on the caste system in India drew many bitter comments from his opponents. He refused to be silent and in this poem he answers his critics. Typical of **lyric poetry**, this poem speaks to a single emotional issue.

L'envoi

When earth's last picture is painted, and the tubes are twisted and dried,
When the oldest colors have faded, and the youngest critic has died,
We shall rest, and, faith, we shall need it—lie down for an aeon or two,
Till the Master of All Good Workmen shall set us to work anew!

And those that were good will be happy; they shall sit in a golden chair;
They shall splash at a ten-league canvas with brushes of comets' hair;
They shall find real saints to draw from—Magdalene, Peter, and Paul;
They shall work for an age at a sitting and never be tired at all!

And only the Master shall praise us, and only the Master shall blame;
And no one shall work for money, and no one shall work for fame;
But each for the joy of working, and each, in his separate star,
Shall draw the Thing as he sees It for the God of Things as They Are!

—*Rudyard Kipling*

Prose and Poetry

Name _____ Date _____

Acrostic

Acrostic poetry is written so that the theme of the poem is spelled out by the first letter in each line. Reading down across the lines produces the subject of the poem, thus it is called acrostic. The mood of the poem should match the theme.

Happy New Year

Here we are nearing midnight
Addressing ourselves to suspense
Poised on hereafter's horizon
Praising the dawn's eminence.
Yet as we yearn for the future
Nebulous hopes reappear
Embryo dreams died aborning
Winnowed from memory's bier.
Youthful plans that are ageless
Emerge on the future's veiled scope
All promise of their fulfillment
Rest in a single word—HOPE.

Test

Teachers love to torture me
Exams they like especially
Sometimes I think that I must be
Targeted calamity.

—*Helen Ruth Bass*

Frances

(Attributed to George Washington—written for the birthday of a neighbor's child)

From your bright sparkling Eyes I was undone;
Rays, you have; more transparent than the Sun,
Amidst its glory in the rising Day
None can you equal in your bright array;
Constant in your calm and unspotted mind,
Equal to all, but will to none Prove kind,
So knowing, seldom one so Young, you'll Find.

Name _____   Date _____

Ballad

The ballad is one of the oldest and most loved forms of poetry. It is centered around an event, a hero, an emotion, or a cause that is worthy of becoming a legend. There are two main types of ballads: the folk ballad and the literary ballad. In general, the folk ballad has multiple, unknown authors and a set rhythm and verse pattern. The literary ballad, on the other hand, usually has a known author and may have a wide variety of rhythm patterns and verse lengths.

Folk Ballads

Folk ballads have quatrain stanzas and either an iambic or an anapestic rhythm. The rhythm and stanza patterns are established because the same tune can be used for many sets of lyrics, and the same lyrics may be sung to a wide variety of tunes. The rhythm is controlled by the tune it must "fit." To help understand why the rhythm is so fixed, try singing the words of "Mary Had a Little Lamb" to the tune of "The Star Spangled Banner." Using the same "One Size Fits All" rhythm pattern and verse length means that the lyrics and tunes can be interchanged.

A folk ballad often has many anonymous authors; as people travel, they take their ballads with them, altering them to fit new generations, locations, and circumstances. It is not at all unusual to find completely different verses to the same ballad in different locations.

Folk ballad rhythm comes from nature. The earliest ballads had an iambic beat: *te DUM*. These are called the **sea ballads**, not because of their subject matter, but because this rhythm mimics the sound of repeating waves splashing against the shore—*te DUM, te DUM, te DUM*. Many later ballads have an anapestic beat. They are called **horse ballads** because they echo the sound of horse hooves: *te de DUM, te de DUM, te de DUM*. Sea and horse ballads are both types of folk ballads.

Sea Ballad

Many early **sea ballads** have a naval theme, because so much early history centered on the oceans and ocean adventures. A ballad requires a legendary subject, and there were plenty of those at sea. There were great unexpected storms, daring explorations, desperate battles, lost ships, helpless victims, brave heroes, and traitorous scoundrels. Because their name comes from the sea rhythm rather than sea exploits, however, sea ballads are just as apt to be about knights in shining armor, or some undying emotion, or any tragedy or triumph of heroic status. The sea ballad designation is based on the iambic rhythm. Listen for the ocean rhythm in this first verse of "Casabianca" by Felicia D. Hemans. (The heavy stress syllables are in bold print. As you read, exaggerate the stressed syllables to emphasize the sea sound.)

Prose and Poetry

Name _____   Date _____

The **BOY** stood **ON** the **BURN** ing **DECK**   (iambic tetrameter)
Whence **ALL** but **HIM** had **FLED**   (iambic trimeter)
The **FLAME** that **LIT** the **BAT** tle's **WRECK**   (iambic tetrameter)
Shone **ROUND** him **O'ER** the **DEAD**.   (iambic trimeter)

Compare the rhythm of the verse above, which is from a nineteenth-century ballad, with a few of the verses from "Sir Patrick Spens," a thirteenth-century ballad. Sir Patrick, according to legend, was a famous naval hero. Against his better judgment, he was forced by the king to undertake a dangerous voyage in stormy winter seas. He fulfilled his mission of delivering the princess to her wedding, but Sir Patrick and all his brave men were lost at sea on the way home. This tale of bravery and tragedy is true legend material and fulfills that ballad test. Notice that the same tune could be used for both "Casabianca" and "Sir Patrick Spens." (Modern spelling is used.)

"Oh, who is this has done this deed,
    This ill deed done to me,
To send me out this time of year
    To sail upon the sea!"   (fifth verse)

Oh long, long may the ladies stand
    With gold combs in their hair
A'waiting for their own dear lords
    For they'll see them no more.   (tenth verse)

Half o'er, half o'er to Aberdour
    It's fifty fathoms deep,
And there lies good Sir Patrick Spens
    With Scots lords at his feet.   (last verse)

Horse Ballad

Horse ballads are anapestic quatrains with an *abab* or an *abcb* rhyme scheme. They are called horse ballads because their anapestic meter imitates the beat of horse hooves. If you have ever wondered why there are so very many verses to "Home on the Range" and other ballads, just imagine that you are an early western pioneer riding the range. Monotony and boredom have set in because you have been riding since dawn and, except for your horse, you are alone. Almost without thinking, you begin to try to match some of the words to the song you heard by the campfire last night to the only rhythm around—the clip-clop of your horse's walk. (If you don't have a horse, try that slap, slap, clap, imitation of a horse thing with your hands to get the rhythm.) When you can't exactly remember the words, or you don't like those words, or you are just bored, invent new lyrics. Imagine you are in the saddle as you sing (of course, out loud!):

Name _____ Date _____

Oh, now **GIVE** me a **HOME** where the **BUFF** a lo **ROAM**   (anapestic tetrameter)
Where the **DEER** and the **ANT** e lope **PLAY**   (anapestic trimeter)
And where **SEL** dom is **HEARD** a dis **COUR** a ging **WORD**   (anapestic tetrameter)
And the **SKY** is not **CLOU** dy all **DAY**.   (anapestic trimeter)

So you give me a land where the bright diamond sand
Flows leisurely down to the stream
And the maiden white swan goes a'gliding along
Like a maid in a heavenly dream.

When I stand here at night and the heavens are bright
With a light from the glittering stars
And I am so amazed that I ask as I gaze
If their glory exceeds that of ours.

This ballad has many, many more verses and a chorus. This chorus is repeated after every verse, or every other verse, or whenever the singer desires.

Chorus:

Home, home on the range,
Where the deer and the antelope play
And where seldom is heard a discouraging word
And the sky is not cloudy all day.

One further fact about all folk ballads must be mentioned: Never, NEVER, **NEVER** try to read one silently. There is something inhuman about trying to remain hushed or still while reading "Hoop E Ti Yi Yo, Git Along Little Doggies." The bravery it would take to sit quietly in a sedate library while reading a volume of folk ballads would be enough to inspire a new ballad!

Literary Ballad

The **literary ballad** does not have the rhythm or rhyme restrictions of a folk ballad. It fulfills its ballad requirement by telling a story about an event, hero, emotion, or cause of legendary status. From Henry Wadsworth Longfellow's account of the midnight ride of Paul Revere to a calypso of the West Indies, from the protests of Joan Baez to street rap, a literary ballad can take many forms. It usually has an identified author and is less likely than the folk ballad to be intended for singing. Those that are sung usually have music written specifically for that set of lyrics. Verses of literary ballads may be of any length and may have any rhythm the author selects as appropriate for that particular story. Comparing verses from two of Rudyard Kipling's many ballads will show some of the numerous differences found in literary ballads.

Name _____   Date _____

The uniform 'e wore was nothin' much before,
An' rather less than 'arf o' that be'ind,
For a piece o' twisty rag an' a goatskin water-bag
Was all the field-equipment 'e could find.
When the sweatin' troop-train lay in a sidin' through the day,
Where the 'eat would make your bloomin' eyebrows crawl,
We shouted "**Harry By!**" till our throats were bricky-dry   (Oh, brother)
Then we wopped 'im 'cause 'e couldn't serve us all.
It was "Din! Din! Din!
You 'eathen, where the mischief 'ave you been?
You put some **juldee** in it,   (speed)
Or I'll **marrow** you this minute   (hit)
If you don't fill up my helmet, Gunga Din!"

—*from "Gunga Din" by Rudyard Kipling*

"What are the bugles blowin' for?" said Files-on-Parade.
"To turn you out, to turn you out," the Color-Sergeant said.
"What makes you look so white, so white?" said Files-on-Parade.
"I'm dreadin' what I've got to watch," the Color-Sergeant said.
"For they're hangin' Danny Deever, you can 'ear the Dead March play,
The regiment's in 'ollow square—they're hangin' him today;
They've taken all his buttons off an' cut his stripes away,"
An' they're hangin' Danny Deever in the mornin'."

—*from "Danny Deever" by Rudyard Kipling*

Name _____   Date _____

Blank Verse

Blank verse is unrhymed iambic pentameter.

Since **blank verse** is unrhymed poetry, it depends on its imagery to set it apart from prose, and on its metric pattern to set it apart from free verse. It has no set stanza pattern, often having stanzas (sometimes called verse paragraphs) of differing lengths within the same poem. Shakespeare's plays are in blank verse, more or less. He uses iambic pentameter frequently enough that it seems intended, but he did not allow it to interfere with his thought. In this excerpt from *Macbeth*, the "true" iambic pentameter lines are marked with >, but note how near the other lines are to that metric pattern.

    Tomorrow, and tomorrow, and tomorrow,
> Creeps in this petty pace from day to day,
    To the last syllable of recorded time;
> And all our yesterdays have lighted fools
    The way to dusty death. Out, out, brief candle;
    Life's but a walking shadow; a poor player,
> That struts and frets his hour upon the stage,
> And then is heard no more; it is a tale
    Told by an idiot, full of sound and fury,
    Signifying nothing.

           —from Macbeth *by William Shakespeare*

True Answer

I wrote a verse the other day that told
The things I didn't have the nerve to speak.
I poured out all my heartache and my hurt,
I wept in words and cried in manuscript.
The meter somehow managed to absterge
The wound that wound across my inner dream.
There's therapeutic value in a verse.
Iambically, I sutured up my soul.

           —*Helen Ruth Bass*

Name _____   Date _____

Didactic Poetry

Didactic poetry is any verse written to teach a specific, academic lesson.

Rhyme is easily recalled and even small children can remember nursery rhymes because they rhyme. Older children remember facts they might otherwise have difficulty with in the same way. Here are some examples of **didactic poetry**:

Our Presidents
First stands the lofty Washington,
The noble, great, immortal one.
The elder Adams next we see,
And Jefferson comes number three;
Then Madison is fourth, you know,
The fifth one on the list, Monroe;
The sixth, then Adams comes again,
And Jackson seventh in the train.
Van Buren eighth upon the line
And Harrison counts number nine.
The tenth is Tyler in his turn,
And Polk the eleventh, as we learn.
The twelfth is Taylor in rotation,
The thirteenth Fillmore in succession;
The fourteenth, Pierce, has been selected,
Buchanan, fifteenth, is elected;
Sixteenth, Lincoln rules the nation;
Johnson, seventeenth, fills the station;
As the eighteenth Grant two terms serves;
Nineteenth, Hayes our honor preserves;
Twentieth, Garfield becomes our head;
Twenty-first, Arthur succeeds the dead;
Then Cleveland next was selected;
Twenty-third, Harrison's elected;
Twenty-fourth, Cleveland is recalled;
Twenty-fifth, McKinley twice installed;
Twenty-sixth, Roosevelt, strenuous, firm;
Taft, twenty-seventh, serves his term;
Twenty-eighth, Wilson holds the place,
A nation's problems has to face.

—*Author Unknown*

Columbus
Columbus sailed the ocean blue
In fourteen hundred ninety two.

Sulphuric Acid
Little Johnny took a drink
But he will drink no more,
For what he thought was H_2O
Was H_2SO_4.

Spelling
Write I before E
Except after C
Or when it says "A"
As in *neigh* and in *weigh*.

Name _____   Date _____

Dramatic Poetry

Dramatic poetry has a character or characters who speak in conversational form.

In **dramatic poetry**, if there is only one person speaking, it is called a **dramatic monologue**. Shakespeare's soliloquies are dramatic monologues. With two or more in conversation, the poetry is called a **dramatic dialogue**. The term *dramatic* is most often used as a second descriptive identification of a poem. Ballads, for example, may be dramatic monologues or dramatic dialogues. Here is an example of dramatic poetry.

The Blind Men and the Elephant

It was six men of Indostan to learning much inclined,
Who went to see the elephant (though all of them were blind),
That each by observation might satisfy his mind.
    The First approached the elephant, and, happening to fall
    Against his broad and sturdy side, at once began to bawl:
    "God bless me! but the elephant is nothing but a wall!"
The Second, feeling of the tusk cried: "Ho! what have we here
So very round and smooth and sharp? to me 'tis very clear
This wonder of an elephant is very like a spear!"
    The Third approached the animal, and, happening to take
    The squirming trunk within his hands, thus boldly up and spake:
    "I see," quoth he, "the elephant is very like a snake!"
The Fourth reached out his eager hand, and felt about the knee:
"What most this wondrous beast is like is mighty plain," quoth he;
" 'Tis clear enough the elephant is very like a tree."
    The Fifth, who chanced to touch the ear, said: "E'en the blindest man
    Can tell what this resembles most; deny the fact who can,
    This marvel of an elephant is very like a fan!"
The Sixth no sooner had begun about the beast to grope,
Than, seizing on the swinging tail that fell within his scope,
"I see," quoth he, "the elephant is very like a rope!"
    And so the men of Indostan disputed loud and long,
    Each in his own opinion exceeding stiff and strong,
    Though each was partly in the right, and all were in the wrong!
So, oft in theologic wars the disputants, I ween,
Rail on in utter ignorance of what each other mean,
And prate about an elephant not one of them has seen!

—John Godfrey Saxe

Prose and Poetry

Name _____ Date _____

Elegy

 An elegy is a poem of mourning that is written in memory of someone.

Most **elegies** are very personal, written after the death of a loved one. Some are more impersonal, grieving for a lost cause or for a downtrodden class, but the expression of emotion is still deep and profound.

Lincoln's death is the subject of many elegies. Walt Whitman wrote one in memory of Lincoln. He used a story about a ship's captain killed just before the battle was won. This is the last verse of his elegy.

 O Captain! My Captain!

My Captain does not answer, his lips are pale and still,
My father does not feel my arm, he has no pulse nor will,
The ship is anchored safe and sound, its voyage is closed and done,
From fearful trip the victor ship comes in with object won;
Exult O shores, and ring O bells! But I with mournful tread,
Walk the deck my Captain lies, fallen cold and dead.

—*Walt Whitman*

Here is an elegy by William Wordsworth:

 Lucy

She dwelt among the untrodden ways
Beside the springs of Dove;
A maid whom there were none to praise,
And very few to love.

A violet by a mossy stone
Half hidden from the eye!
Fair as a star, when only one
Is shining in the sky.

She lived unknown, and few could know
When Lucy ceased to be;
But she is in her grave, and O,
The difference to me!

—*William Wordsworth*

Name _____ Date _____

Epigram

An epigram is a very short, humorous poem. It may have any stanza pattern or rhyme scheme.

The Optimist

The optimist fell ten stories
And at each window bar
He shouted out to all his friends,
"I'm all right so far!"

—*Author Unknown*

The Grass

You water grass to make it grow
Then you find out you have to mow!

—*Author Unknown*

For a New Year

Let's make the whole world over;
No, not quite all, that's true.
A few things were right to begin with,
Like God—and myself—and you.

—*Leonard Hinton*

Advice to Small Children

Eat no green apples or you'll droop,
Be careful not to get the croup,
Avoid the chicken-pox and such,
And don't fall out of windows much.

—*Edward Anthony*

Prose and Poetry

Name _____ Date _____

Epitaph

An epitaph is a brief poem suitable for engraving on a cemetery headstone.

Requiem
Under the wide and starry sky,
    Dig the grave and let me lie.
    Glad did I live and gladly die,
And I laid me down with a will.

This be the verse you grave for me:
    Here he lies where he longed to be,
    Home is the sailor, home from the sea,
And the hunter home from the hill.

                    —*Robert Louis Stevenson*

Leona
Alas,
Our Love
Now Dwells
Above

Willy
Depart
My Heart

    —*Author Unknown*

Humorous Epitaphs

Here lie G. Whilliken's friends, all five.
He took them along when he learned to drive.

Stranger, pause and shed a tear
For one who leaves no mourners,
    D. F. Sapp reposes here;
Known for cutting corners.

                —*Author Unknown*

Dot Com did drown
Her fate she met
While surfing on
The Internet.

Prose and Poetry

Name _____   Date _____

Free Verse

Free verse has no rhyme scheme and no stanza pattern. Without these usual poetry elements, it depends entirely on the power of its imagery to be classified as poetry.

A Long-haired Boy

a long-haired boy, a girl
talked hand in hand in a sun-soaked field
for a long time, she talked, he thought
for a long time, he talked, she thought.
   she stood up, their eyes met,
   he caught her arm, she turned
   into the sun, head held high, she walked
   he stood, thought, with her in his mind
     walked, into the sun, not following.

         —William Wayland Halbert, Jr.

Apparition

Your name . . .
             I can't remember your name . . .
Impulsively, you perch on the rim of my memory
And waver there in precarious balance.
You implore me to reach across the gap
And solidify you into firm consciousness
Your identity—
            darts past—
Then hovers in tantalizing proximity, and
           —even as I grab
It vanishes into the abyss of nihility.

Interminably, You mock and thwart me.
You skip across all chronological spans
Until I know not whether you belong
In past . . . . or future.
Intangible Adversary of Contentment!!!
Some consolation lies in the vengeful vision that,
Perhaps—
       Somewhere—

               I haunt you, too!!!
              —Helen Ruth Bass

Prose and Poetry

Name _____   Date _____

Haiku

Haiku is a 3-line nature poem of 17 syllables, divided so that the first and third lines have 5 syllables each and the middle line has 7 syllables.

Haiku originated in Japan. Examples have been preserved from as early as the thirteenth century. It reached a high point in the seventeenth century, when the Japanese poet Basho perfected it as an art form. Kikaku, a Japanese female poet, was a student of Basho and Chiyo and wrote at about the same time.

An essential element of Haiku is that a season—or something that indicates a specific season—must be mentioned. A second essential element is that the poet suggests an idea through observation, but does not actually draw a conclusion. It is left to the reader to think about what is said and draw a personal conclusion. One of Kikaku's and two of Chiyo's verses illustrate content but, because they have been translated from Japanese, the syllable and line requirements are dropped since these restrictions are applied only to the language of origin.

The Cricket Wails

(translation)

Perchance the cricket is bemoaning
    Her husband eaten by a cat.

—*Kikaku*

The Morning-Glory

(translation)

A morning-glory having taken
The well-bucket, I begged for water.

—*Chiyo*

The Bright Moon

(translation)

In any garments we appear
Beautiful under the bright moon.

Because of its simplicity, Haiku is a favorite for beginning poets to compose. The line spacing is optional, but the following shows how lines and syllables might be divided when Haiku is written in English:

Beauty

Butterfly beauty
    fades away, our memories
        should live forever.

—*Student R*

Light Verse

Light verse is any poem whose intent is comedy or humor. Since that description will include epigrams, limericks, and other poem types, it may be used as a second identification for another type of poem.

The Pessimist

Nothing to do but work,
Nothing to eat but food;
Nothing to wear but clothes
To keep one from going nude.

Nothing to breathe but air,
Quick as a flash 'tis gone;
Nowhere to fall but off,
Nowhere to stand but on.

Nothing to comb but hair,
Nowhere to sleep but in bed;
Nothing to weep but tears,
Nothing to bury but dead.

Nothing to sing but songs;
Ah, well, alas! alack!
Nowhere to go but out,
Nowhere to come but back.

Nothing to see but sights,
Nothing to quench but thirst;
Nothing to have but what we've got;
Thus thro' life we are cursed.

Nothing to strike but a gait;
Everything moves that goes,
Nothing at all but common sense
Can ever withstand these woes.

—*Ben King*

Rock-a-Bye Chickee

My old oak tree stood listlessly
No movement to be seen
And then a breeze swept through its leaves
And rippled through its green.

From where it hung the birdhouse swung
A pendulum in motion
Just like a boat that bobbed afloat
Upon a leafy ocean.

The birdhouse door revealed that four
Young chicks were bunched inside
Their cheeps of fear made it quite clear
They didn't like the ride.

At treetop high in bough-tossed sky
Those baby birds were rocking
Yet not their fall I feared at all
But something much more shocking.

No walk for me beneath that tree
A safer path I'll pick !
A house that moves might be what proves
Beware a seasick chick!

—*Helen Ruth Bass*

Name _____   Date _____

Limerick

 A limerick is a five-line jingle whose purpose is humor. It usually has an *aabba* rhyme scheme, with the first, second, and fifth lines of either anapestic or amphibrach trimeter, and the third and fourth lines of anapestic dimeter. The rhythm, rhyme scheme, and humor are all expected components. Wordplay is often incorporated into the humor. The same verse will often have multiple, anonymous authors and it will endure through both geographical and generational changes. Here are some of those anonymous examples:

There was a young lady from Niger
Who smiled as she rode on the tiger.
They returned from the ride
With the lady inside,
And the smile on the face of the tiger!

A tutor who tooted the flute
Tried to teach two young tooters to toot
Said the two of the tutor,
"Is it harder to toot, or
To tutor two tooters to toot?"

As a beauty I am not a star
There are others more handsome by far
But my face I don't mind it
For I am behind it
It's the people in front that I jar!

There was a young lady of Lynn
Who was so exceedingly thin
That when she essayed
To drink lemonade
She slipped through the straw and fell in!

Name _____ Date _____

Ode

An ode is a lengthy lyrical poem of praise. It may have any rhyme scheme, rhythm pattern, or stanza pattern.

In the following excerpt from "Ode on a Grecian Urn," Keats describes some of the many scenes painted on the side of an ancient urn. He makes the point that, for the characters painted in the scenes, time is frozen. They will never age, nor will they achieve any goal they were seeking at the moment they were captured by the artist. This praise of the beauty of the urn, coupled with the reflections and conclusions inspired by their beauty, are typical of an **ode**.

Heard melodies are sweet, but those unheard
Are sweeter, therefore, ye soft pipes, play on;
Not to the sensual ear, but, more endear'd,
Pipe to the spirit ditties of no tone: . . .
Fair youth, beneath the trees, thou canst not leave
Thy song, nor ever can those trees be bare;
Bold Lover, never, never canst thou kiss
Though winning near the goal—yet, do not grieve;
She cannot fade, though thou hast not thy bliss,
For ever wilt thou love, and she be fair! . . .

—from "Ode on a Grecian Urn" by John Keats

Hail to thee, blithe Spirit!
Bird thou never wert,
That from Heaven, or near it,
Pourest thy full heart
In profuse strains
of unpremeditated art.

—from "To a Skylark"
by Percy Bysshe Shelley

Stern Daughter of the Voice of God!
O Duty! if that name thou love
Who art a light to guide, a rod
To check the erring, and reprove;
Thou, who art victory and law
When empty terrors overawe,

—from "Ode to Duty"
by William Wordsworth

Prose and Poetry

Name _____   Date _____

Ogden Nash wrote many satirical poems. The following is a satirical ode. In it, he has combined several well-known odes for his targets. The title refers to Wordworth's "Ode to Duty." The last two lines mock the last lines from "Voluntaries" by Ralph Waldo Emerson:

When Duty whispers low, ***Thou must***,
    The youth replies, ***I can.***

Kind of an Ode to Duty

O Duty,
Why hast thou not the visage of a sweetie or a cutie?
Why glitter thy spectacles so ominously?
Why art thous so different from Venus
And why do thou and I have so few interests mutually in
        common between us?
Why art thou fifty percent martyr
And fifty-one percent Tartar?

Why is it thy unfortunate wont
To try to attract people by calling on them either to leave undone
        the deeds they like, or to do the deeds they don't?
Why art thou so like an April post-mortem
On something that died in the ortumn?
Above all, why dost thou continue to hound me?
Why art thou always albatrossly hanging around me?

Thou so ubiquitous,
And I so iniquitous.
I seem to be the one person in the world thou are perpetually
        preaching at who or to who;
Whatever looks like fun, there art thou standing between me
        and it, calling yoo-hoo.
O Duty, Duty!
How noble a man should I be hadst thou the visage of a
        sweetie or a cutie!
But as it is thou art so much forbiddinger than a Wodehouse
        hero's forbiddingest aunt
That in the words of the poet, When Duty whispers low, ***Thou must***,
        this erstwhile youth replies, ***I just can't.***

                                                    —*Ogden Nash*

Name _____   Date _____

Parody

Parody poetry is based on a poem that is so well known that a mimic of its rhythm, rhyme scheme, or phraseology is immediately recognized. The topic may be totally different from the original poem or it may have a different view or slant on the same topic. One Parody on "The Night Before Christmas," for example, begins with:

" 'Twas the night before Christmas and all through the flat,
   Not a creature was stirring, not even a rat."

Original poem

Trees

I think that I shall never see
A poem lovely as a tree
A tree whose hungry mouth is pressed
Against the earth's sweet flowing breast;
A tree that looks at God all day
And lifts her leafy arms to pray
A tree that may in summer wear
A nest of robins in her hair
Upon whose bosom snow has lain
Who intimately lives with rain,
Poems are made by fools like me
But only God can make a tree.

—*Joyce Kilmer*

Parody

TVs

I think that I shall never see
Things like they show on my TV.
A mouthwash that, used once a day,
Will make a lover come your way;
A bar of soap that's guaranteed
To keep you from all odors freed;
A bleach that cleans the deepest stain;
A beer that tastes just like champagne.
One truth we cannot minimize,
It really pays to advertise;
These brands are bought by fools like me,
But only work on my TV.

—*Helen Ruth Bass*

Original rhyme

Mary Had a Little Lamb

Mary had a little lamb
His fleece was white as snow,
And everywhere that Mary went
Her lamb was sure to go.

—*Anonymous*

Parody

Merry Had a Little Lamb

Merry had a little lamb
His fleece was black as soot,
And everywhere that lamby went
His sooty foot he put.

—*Anymouse*

Prose and Poetry

Name _____   Date _____

Pastoral

Pastoral poetry praises nature or rural life. It can have any stanza pattern or rhyme scheme because this type of poem is based on the content.

June

And what is so rare as a day in June?
Then, if ever, come perfect days;
Then Heaven tries the earth if it be in tune,
And over it softly her warm ear lays;
Whether we look, or whether we listen,
We hear life murmur, or see it glisten;
Every clod feels a stir of might,
An instinct within it that reaches and towers
And, groping blindly above it for light,
Climbs to a soul in grass and flowers;

—from "The Vision of Sir Launfal" by James Russell Lowell

Daffodils

I wandered lonely as a cloud
That floats on high o'er vales and hills,
When all at once I saw a crowd, —
A host of golden daffodils
Beside the lake, beneath the trees,
Fluttering and dancing in the breeze.

Continuous as the stars that shine
And twinkle on the Milky Way,
They stretched in never-ending line
Along the margin of a bay;
Ten thousand saw I, at a glance,
Tossing their heads in sprightly dance.

The waves beside them danced, but they
Outdid the sparkling waves in glee;
A poet could not but be gay
In such a jocund company;
I gazed—and gazed—but little thought
What wealth the show to me had brought.

For oft, when on my couch I lie,
In vacant or in pensive mood,
They flash upon that inward eye
Which is the bliss of solitude;
And then my heart with pleasure fills,
And dances with the daffodils.

—William Wordsworth

Prose and Poetry

Name _____   Date _____

Satire

Satire attacks folly by ridicule or playful sarcasm. It may have any rhythm pattern or rhyme scheme, depending on content for its classification.

Often **satire** attempts to point out a humorous twist to a serious situation. Sometimes an author will feel that some minor situation has been taken too seriously and will attempt, through humor, to set it in more proper perspective. This is the type of humor in the first example below. Have you ever known someone whose life was centered on counting calories? Apparently, the author knew someone like this.

Methuselah

Methuselah ate what he found on his plate,
And never, as people do now,
Did he note the amount of the calorie count;
He ate it because it was chow.
He wasn't disturbed as at dinner he sat,
Devouring a roast or a pie,
To think it was lacking in granular fat
Or a couple of vitamins shy.
He carefully chewed each species of food,
Unmindful of troubles or fears
Lest his health might be hurt
By some fancy dessert;
And he lived over nine hundred years!

—Author Unknown

The Perils of Thinking

A centipede was happy quite,
Until a frog in fun
Said, "Pray which leg comes after which?"
This raised her mind to such a pitch,
She lay distracted in the ditch
Considering how to run.

—Author Unknown

Name _____   Date _____

Sonnet

The sonnet, a poem of deep emotion, is a 14-line verse of iambic pentameter. It is generally recognized as having the most rigid requirements and being the most difficult to compose of all poetry forms. The poet has exactly 140 syllables to introduce, describe, and draw a moral conclusion on the chosen topic. The presentation must be plain enough to understand and it must be obscure enough to provoke thought. The topic must be worthy of such an endeavor.

There are two types of sonnets: the **Italian**, or **Petrarchan sonnet** and the **English**, or **Shakespearean sonnet**. The requirements of emotion, syllabication, and content apply to both. The difference between the two types is evidenced in the rhyme scheme.

The Italian, or Petrarchan sonnet has an octave-sestet division of *abbaabba-cdecde,* with the scene shift, if any, following this rhyme division. Some variation is allowed in the rhyme scheme except that the first octave is limited to a pair of rhymes (*a* and *b*) and in the final sestet, the last two lines may not rhyme. (This could be *abababab cdecde* or *aabbaabb cdecde,* etc.) An example of the Italian sonnet is this well-known one written by Elizabeth Barrett Browning.

Sonnets from the Portuguese
XLIII

How do I love thee? Let me count the ways.
I love thee to the depth and breadth and height
My soul can reach, when feeling out of sight
For the ends of Being and Ideal Grace.
I love thee to the level of every day's
Most quiet need, by sun and candle-light.
I love thee freely, as men strive for Right;
I love thee purely, as they turn from Praise.
I love thee with the passion put to use
In my old griefs, and with my childhood's faith.
I love thee with a love I seemed to lose
With my lost saints, — I love thee with the breath,
Smiles, tears of all my life! — and, if God choose,
I shall but love thee better after death.

                    —*Elizabeth Barrett Browning*

Name _____   Date _____

The English, or Shakespearean sonnet has three quatrains and a couplet of *ababcdcdefefgg,* with the scene shift following the rhyme division. The first quatrain, *abab*, sets the scene. The second quatrain, *cdcd,* disturbs the scene. The third quatrain, *efef,* reflects on the problem. The final couplet, *gg,* moralizes on the issue raised. An example of a sonnet that follows this pattern is found in "Tap Root."

Tap Root

1. It's Christmas Eve and there in splendor bright
2. My handwork gleams in sumptuous display.
3. The tree is gowned in tinsel, laced by light —
4. Gay ornaments relay each dancing ray.
5. But spangles sprinkled on its shroud won't veil
6. That, underneath, the tree is crucified —
7. Its severed stalk impaled by rusted nail,
8. Life's tap root shorn, in emptiness it died.
9. The ornamented surface of that bier
10. Reflects my hollow life so ruthlessly —
11. An empty soul encased in gilt veneer
12. Inside, I'm dead, just like that rootless tree.
13. Oh, God, before tomorrow, I implore
14. Thy root of Faith to fill my empty core.

—*Helen Ruth Bass*

In accord with the requirements for an English sonnet:

Lines 1–4 set the scene. In these lines, the tree is pretty, bright, and festive.

Lines 5–8 disturb the scene. In these lines the tree is dead, wrapped in a shroud.

Lines 9–12 reflect on the problem. The author is compared to the dead, empty tree.

Lines 13–14 moralize on the issue. The author prays for faith to replace emptiness.

Although other poetry patterns have flexibility, the requirement for sonnets remain pretty constant. A poem of more or fewer syllables, or one that is not iambic, is simply not a sonnet. Because of this rigid insistence on every little detail and because they are considered to be so difficult to write, the sonnet is considered by many as the official poetry of love. (A suitor who thinks enough of his sweetheart to compose something for her that is this difficult must really care.) At least, so they say!

Name _____   Date _____

Wordplay

Wordplay is the humorous use of alternate definitions, puns, or homonyms. Their humor is rooted in the manipulation of language or, simply, the play with words. Wordplay can have any stanza pattern, rhyme scheme, or rhythm because its classification is based on the content.

Of Chicks and Men

While some say we're kin to monkeys, I must beg to disagree
For the bond we have with CHICKENS seems the closer one to me.

Now an OLD HEN or a BIDDY you can recognize on sight
Since she HATCHES senile intrigue, then she CACKLES with delight.

And the man who's CHICKENHEARTED knows the right to CROW comes when
He CLIPS THE WINGS of someone who's MAD AS AN OLD WET HEN.

You've all met the STRUTTING ROOSTER whose fine ego needs no boost
'Cause he knows a HENPECKED husband will never RULE THE ROOST.

A CUTE CHICK is a FLAPPER, she's the YOUNG SPRING CHICKEN type,
And HARD-BOILED with RUFFLED FEATHERS best describes a mean old gripe.

Now the SCRAMBLED brains of DUMB CLUCKS are still found abundantly,
While still truly SCARCE AS HEN'S TEETH, does a GOOD EGG seem to be.

"Oh, he CHICKENED OUT," "He EGGED HIM ON," "He FLEW THE COOP,"
    we say
And those who work for CHICKEN FEED have bills that they can't pay.

The saying, "He's an EGGHEAD," we reserve for brilliant men
(Though I'm much more accustomed to some EGG upon my chin!)

Now if these HEN SCRATCHINGS jar you then your pardon I will beg
Since there's nothing more pathetic than a poem that LAYS AN EGG!

                                                    —*Helen Ruth Bass*

Name _____   Date _____

Now look at these excerpted verses from "Faithless Nellie Gray," a lengthy poem by Thomas Hood. It is quite out of character for Hood to write this type of poem. He is better known for more somber poems, such as "The Song of the Shirt." It is believed his serious poetry had an influence on the Industrial Revolution.

Ben Battle was a soldier bold,
And used to war's alarms;
But a cannon-ball took off his legs
So he laid down his arms.

Now as they bore him off the field,
Said he, "Let others shoot;
For here I leave my second leg,
And the Forty-second Foot."   (the name of his regiment)

Said she, I loved a soldier once,
For he was blithe and brave;
But I will never have a man
With both legs in the grave.

"Before you had those timber toes
Your love I did allow;
But then, you know, you stand upon
Another footing now."

"O false and fickle Nellie Gray!
I know why you refuse;
Though I've no feet, some other man
Is standing in my shoes."

And there he hung till he was dead
As any nail in town;
For, though distress had cut him up,
It could not cut him down.

—from "Faithless Nellie Gray
(A Pathetic Ballad)" by Thomas Hood

Name _____ Date _____

Explication of Poetry

Explication means to EXPlain all the impLICATIONs of the poetic elements in a verse.

Explications take a variety of forms. Almost any type of examination of poetry can be called an explication. One might study the use of rhyme, one might examine the effect of meter, another might look for the influence of figures of speech, and still another might include all of the above. Length and form of the explication may vary as much as content. All of them are "right," so do not expect one explication to predict what the next one may require. Because of these diversities, the one universal rule that applies to all explications is—

Whatever is assigned is correct.

Some things, however, will remain constant. The rules for rhyme and meter, for example, will be the same. Figure of speech classifications will not change. What changes is whether or not they should be part of a specific explication. This section contains tips and examples of functions that any explicator might need. The list of suggested questions and the elements found in the sample poem, for example, are given as methods that an explicator can adapt to any assignment.

Tips on understanding poetry:

Read slowly. Drift with the flow of the poet's pace.

Read aloud. Let the poet speak to you with the inflection and tone of your own voice. Listen to yourself.

Read kindly. Try to get the words to rhyme, the meter to beat, and the emotions to emerge. Read in the way you would like that poet to read *your* poem.

Read with an open mind. If you feel inclined to disagree with the poet, remember that you have to understand exactly what you disagree with in order to refute it. Don't "paddle upstream" trying to get the poet to say what you would say or the way you would say it. Remember that this poem has already been written. You can't change it. If you disagree with it, write your own poem. Remember that you can appreciate the expression even when you disagree with the thought. (Most "I don't understand" protests actually begin with "I don't agree.")

Reread, several times. Be patient.

Tips on writing a report:

Before beginning your review, decide if this report is to be an analysis or an opinion. An analysis will examine the expression from the original author's point of view. An opinion will reflect your reaction to that expression. If you are giving your opinion, decide whether you are reacting to the idea of the author or to the mechanics of expression, the poetry itself.

Remember that the statements you make often say more about you than about the poem, so have a little class. Show a little style. Say something about the uniformity

Prose and Poetry

Name _____   Date _____

of his meter or the identity of his or her point of view (Sure you can!) rather than

something as trite as "I like it" or as crude as "It stinks."

Tips on questions:

One good way to report on literature, whether explicating a poem or reviewing prose, is to pose and answer a series of questions about the work. If we ask good questions and find good answers, the report is simply a matter of organizing and reporting our findings.

What is a good question? While it may be true there is no such thing as a bad question, there *is* such a thing as a good question. First, it requires that the asker knows exactly what information is being sought. Suppose I send you out to look for a thurkemthrottle. I need one badly and have promised you a small fortune if you will locate one for me. You rush out to find one and, guess what? You don't know what a thurkemthrottle is. If you don't understand what you are looking for, how will you know if you find it? The first requirement for a good question, then, is knowing enough about the subject to be able to recognize when an answer has been found. The questioner must then be able to understand and evaluate the answer.

Good answers, also, have requirements. Suppose you ask me what a thurkemthrottle is so you can seek that small fortune I promised. I answer you by explaining that it is anything that thurkemthrates. This may be quite true, but have I given you any additional information? Would you call this a good answer? Since it will not help you find what to look for to find a thurkemthrottle, it has no value, even though it is a "true" answer. This is an example of why no form of a term is ever used to define the term

itself. A dictionary is allowed to do this only because the term itself is defined properly elsewhere in the same dictionary, usually on the same page. As we consider the questions an explicator might ask and the report his answers to those questions will generate, it is important to remember that it may not help just to find **an answer**, we need to seek **good answers**. (Don't waste your time, by the way, looking for any thurkemthrottles. I invented the word and the thing itself does not exist. In addition, I have no fortune either large or small, so let's move on to something you can do.)

The questions that are suggested in this section should be used as opening questions. There is an ancient proverb that states "The larger the circle of light, the greater the circumference of darkness." In other words, the more we find out about a subject, the more questions we can find to ask. Use the questions that are helpful and feel free to ask additional questions that these may suggest.

The questions are divided by subject sections. If you find questions you do not understand, or you have difficulty in finding or understanding the answers, try reviewing the corresponding subject section in this guide. Remember that it takes only one cloudy sentence or one vague statement to ruin a report, so if, after reviewing that section, you are not sure you understand either the question or its answer, omit it from your report. Since all of the questions will not apply to all situations, omit those that are not germane to your report.

Name _____   Date _____

Tips on finding elements:

If the items are searched for individually, they are easier to find. Assonance, for instance, is not something that announces itself too readily. It is easier to detect if it is the subject of a specific search. Compare finding elements to a manhunt by detectives. The subject is more likely to be found if the searcher has a picture and a suspected location than if the searcher just stands on a street corner waiting to see if some wanted person might wander past.

Notice that a specific reference is given for each item on the partial list of elements. Finding examples is an essential step in any explication. Which items might be used and whether or not to find more is usually determined by the assignment that is given. If more material is needed, the list of suggested questions for an explicator might be useful. Feel free to add to the ones suggested. Areas such as thought, person, setting, style, and slant have not been explored in the sample search for elements, but could be identified in the same way if desired. What is the central thought or theme of the poem? Is there an obvious slant to the poem? Keep asking specific questions and finding specific answers and your report almost will write itself.

Name _____   Date _____

Sample Questions for the Explicator

Senses: How does the author involve the senses? Which senses are directly involved? Why would the author select these particular senses for involvement in this thought? Is some sense omitted that might have added to the expression of the thought?

Mood: What is the predominant mood of the poem? Does the mood shift? Why? Did the poet choose an appropriate way to help the reader understand the mood? Is the mood routine or unusual for this subject?

Point of view: What is the author's point of view? Is it necessary? Honest? Ironic? Is the poem a worthy expression of and for this point of view? Is the surface expression the real point of view? Is this poem typical for this poet? Why or why not?

Figures of speech: What figures of speech are used? Are they effective? Do they "fit" the thought, mood, etc.? Do they help create clarity or do they cause confusion? Do they seem contrived? Are they original? Are they clichés?

Pattern: What is the rhyme scheme? What is the stanza pattern? Are they appropriate for the thought? Why (or why not) select this pattern for this thought? Does the scene shift match the rhyme shift? Is the stanza pattern uniform and sustained? Is rhyme scheme uniform and sustained?

Type of poem: What type of poem is this? Why (or why not) select this framework for this thought? Is there another type of poem that might fit this thought?

Melody: What elements of melody are used—Onomatopoeia? Alliteration? Assonance? Rhyme? Does rhyme limit the poet? Is it stilted or trite rhyme? What is the value of the rhyme (or lack of it) in this poem? What types of rhyme are used—Single? Double? Triple? Internal? Imperfect? Near rhyme? Is the rhyme sustained throughout the poem?

Rhythm: What is the effect of the rhythm pattern on the mood? Is the type of rhythm appropriate for the thought? Is it a pronounced or subtle rhythm? Is it sustained? Is there inversion? If so, is it deliberate or careless? Is there caesura? If so, does it enhance the effect or result from poor word choice? Which element is stronger, rhythm or rhyme?

Name _____   Date _____

Samples of Explication Elements
The Ballad of the Hall

1 The boy stood by the classroom door
2 And moaned with mortal woe
3 His next course was across the hall
4 And time had come to go!

5 His nerves were shot and fear a knot
6 That tightened up his breath
7 But through the crush he had to push
8 Though it could mean his death!

9 But as he paused another thought
10 Did jerk him like a rein
11 His locker held a book he'd need
12 He staggered with the pain!

13 "I'll go," he cried, "I'll carry on.
14 No fear shall conquer me!"
15 And out he plunged into that stream
16 Of kind humanity!

17 It swallowed him and passed him on
18 In peristaltic wave
19 Then spewed him out against the wall
20 So broken, yet so brave!

21 He grabbed and dialed the hostile knob
22 And then, in pure frustration,
23 His voice rang out, "Oh, Brother, I
24 Forgot my combination!"

25 Though kicked and hit and shoved about
26 In spite of his despair
27 He fumbled till the lock came free
28 And books spilled everywhere!

29 Then gathering both nerves and books
30 He dived back in the tide
31 Like Moses parting the Red Sea
32 He reached the other side!

33 And, though in glory brief he stood,
34 The fight was far from o'er.
35 He knew that just one hour hence
36 He'd forge that horde once more!

FIGURES OF SPEECH

Apostrophe
Line 23—His brother, even if he has one, is not there to answer.

Hyperbole
Line 2—His woe is far short of fatal (mortal).
Line 8—Death greatly exaggerates crowd action.

Irony
Line 16—Humanity is not kind at all to the boy. Calling it kind is sarcastic, the opposite of the truth.

Literary Allusion
Line 31—Moses and Red Sea are Bible references.

Metaphor
Line 29—Nerves are compared to solid objects.
Line 30—"Dived" and "tide" compare crowd to ocean.

Metonymy
Line 3—The course is not across the hall, classroom where it is taught is across the hall.

Personification
Line 21—Knob is an inanimate object, cannot be hostile.

Simile
Line 10—This uses "like" to compare unlike things, thought is inanimate and rein is solid.

RHYTHM

iambic tetrameter—Lines 1 and 3, each verse
1. The **BOY** stood **BY** the **CLASS** room **DOOR**
3. His **NEXT** course **WAS** a **CROSS** the **HALL**

iambic trimeter—Lines 2 and 4, each verse
2. And **MOANED** with **MORT** al **WOE**
4. And **TIME** had **COME** to **GO**!

Prose and Poetry

Name _____   Date _____

Samples of Explication Elements (continued)
The Ballad of the Hall

1 The boy stood by the classroom door
2 And moaned with mortal woe
3 His next course was across the hall
4 And time had come to go!

5 His nerves were shot and fear a knot
6 That tightened up his breath
7 But through the crush he had to push
8 Though it could mean his death!

9 But as he paused another thought
10 Did jerk him like a rein
11 His locker held a book he'd need
12 He staggered with the pain!

13 "I'll go," he cried, "I'll carry on.
14 No fear shall conquer me!"
15 And out he plunged into that stream
16 Of kind humanity!

17 It swallowed him and passed him on
18 In peristaltic wave
19 Then spewed him out against the wall
20 So broken, yet so brave!

21 He grabbed and dialed the hostile knob
22 And then, in pure frustration,
23 His voice rang out, "Oh, Brother, I
24 Forgot my combination!"

25 Though kicked and hit and shoved about
26 In spite of his despair
27 He fumbled till the lock came free
28 And books spilled everywhere!

29 Then gathering both nerves and books
30 He dived back in the tide
31 Like Moses parting the Red Sea
32 He reached the other side!

33 And, though in glory brief he stood,
34 The fight was far from o'er.
35 He knew that just one hour hence
36 He'd forge that horde once more!

MELODY

Alliteration

Line 34—Fight, Far, From—same beginning

Assonance

Line 36—forge, horde, more—same middle sound

Single Rhyme

Second and fourth lines—end words of all verses <u>except</u> sixth verse (Lines 22 and 24) woe, go; rein, pain; me, humanity; wave, brave; etc.

Double Rhyme

Lines 22 and 24—last two consecutive syllables of end words—frus **TRA tion**, combi **NA tion**

Internal Rhyme

Line 5—His nerves were **SHOT** and fear a **KNOT**

Imperfect Rhyme

Line 7—But through the **CRUSH** he had to **PUSH**

Rhyme Scheme

All verses—*abcb*—(*a*—door, *b*—**WOE**, *c*—hall, *b*—**GO**)

Onomatopoeia

Line 2—moaned—sound imitates meaning

TYPE

Satire

Pokes fun at "bravery" required to face crowded hallway
slight sarcasm

Parody

Line 1—"Casabianca" by Felicia D. Hemans begins "The boy stood on the burning deck"

Folk Ballad

Meets <u>metric</u> (alternating iambic tetrameter and trimeter), <u>rhyme</u> (*abcb*), <u>theme</u> (bravery), and <u>stanza</u> requirements (Quatrain—four-line verses)

Prose and Poetry

Sample Answer Key

Part 1: Basic Tools

In most of the exercises, some of the questions have their answers given on the same page. As a general rule, these are simple questions with a single answer. Some students need the assurance of this immediate positive feedback to encourage confident fluency. Other questions have no established, single answer. These questions are designed to allow for variety in grade levels, ability levels, interest areas, and presentation methods. As these factors are expected to vary, so are these answers expected to vary. The responses in this section, therefore, are possible answers, but in no case are they proposed as the answer.

Exercise 1.2 (p. 4)

Situation: a football game:

Tasting stimulus; the snack stand. Tasting responses: (1) buttery popcorn (2) salty french fries. Touching stimulus; the crowd. Touching responses: (1) mashed toe (2) elbowed rib. Hearing stimulus; intercepted pass. Hearing responses: (1) groans of fans (2) cheers of foes. Seeing stimulus; cheer leaders. Seeing responses: (1) red pompons (2) spangled skirts. Smelling stimulus; parking lot. Smelling responses: (1) exhaust fumes (2) acrid hot asphalt.

Exercise 1.4 (p. 6–7)

1. CAR—(First) I knew I should have stopped back there. (Second) You know you should have stopped back there. (Third) He knew he should have stopped back there.

2. SALE—(First) I will need to get there early. (Second) You need to get there before the crowd. (Third) He hoped they would have some left when he got there.

Exercise 1.5 (p. 8)

1. "Casey . . ." Angry, or vengeful, or mad, or furious.

2. "Nick . . ." Happy, or content, or satisfied, or comfortable.

Exercise 1.6 (p. 9)

1. IMPATIENT OR WORRIED—(Three Year Old Boy) Puts thumb in mouth, or whines.

   (Adolescent Girl) Taps foot, or throws book, or slams phone.

   (Grandparent) Paces floor, or rocks rapidly in chair.

2. AFRAID OR SCARED—(Three Year Old Boy) Whimpers, or hides behind chair.

   (Adolescent Girl) Hums nervously, or fusses with hair.

   (Grandparent) Gets very quiet, or eyes dart constantly

Exercise 1.7 (p. 11–12)

1. Person versus Self. Protagonist, Pete—Antagonist, Pete

2. Person versus Nature. Protagonist, Millie—Antagonist, Nature or thirst

3. Person versus Person. Protagonist, Robbie—Antagonist, Jack

Exercise 1.9 (p. 19)

Here are some ideas:

FACTS: The cereal is named QUICK. Each box has two miniature Ambies (latest toy fad) inside. Small box with a big price—but the cover is glitzy. Contains trace amounts of latest diet craze. Add milk and it is ready to eat.

1. Kid's Kapers: With TWO Ambies in every box, QUICK is the fastest way to complete your Ambie collection. You love Ambies and Ambies love QUICK!

2. College Events: Try QUICK because the faster you eat, the faster you can compete!

3. <u>Golden Oldie Notes</u>: Only QUICK will give you a fast balance of your diet and your pocketbook.

Exercise 1.11 (p. 23)

1. O, 2. I, 3. S, 4. I, 5. O, 6. S, 7. I, 8. O, 9. S, 10. O, 11. S, 12. I

Exercise 1.12 (p. 24)

1. Trait: mischievous. Rick laughed as he imagined the look on his father's face when he came down to get the morning paper. Rick had substituted a newspaper written in Chinese for the regular one, and he knew his father would be baffled! What a good April Fools Day joke.

2. Trait: sensitivity; self-consciousness. Risa hurried away from school because she was too embarrassed to go back in after what had happened yesterday. How could she face everybody after falling off the bleachers during the chorus recital?

3. Trait: insecurity. Denzel was furious with himself and furious with his boss, too. His three-month review had been the perfect opportunity for Denzel to assert himself and ask for a raise, but instead he'd found himself agreeing with Mr. Bruno's statement that Denzel needed to be more punctual.

Exercise 1.13 (p. 24)

PARAGRAPH: Maggie was doing her homework at the kitchen table when Juanita, her four year old younger sister, came in for a drink of cold water. It was a hot day but, after taking just one sip, Juanita put the glass down and hurried outside. While Maggie watched, Juanita filled Mr. Dogg's dish with fresh water. When she came skipping back to the kitchen, her smile was so bright that it seemed like her freckles were dancing dots on her chubby face. "There!" she said, "Now Mr. Dogg can have a good cool drink, too."

Examples of things given: <u>O</u>uter Person—four years old, chubby, has freckles. <u>S</u>ocial Person—has a sister, is younger than Maggie. <u>I</u>nner Person—thoughtful or kind or compassionate, etc.—BECAUSE she put the welfare of the dog before her own thirst.

Part 2: Figures of Speech

In most of the exercises, some of the questions have their answers given on the same page. As a general rule, these are simple questions with a single answer. Some students need the assurance of this immediate positive feedback to encourage confident fluency. Other questions have no established, single answer. These questions are designed to allow for variety in grade levels, ability levels, interest areas, and presentation methods. As these factors are expected to vary, so are these answers expected to vary. The responses in this section, therefore, are <u>possible</u> <u>answers</u>, but in no case are they proposed as <u>the answer</u>.

Exercise 2.1 (p. 32)

1. loud laughter—silent meditation (contrasting sound)

2. a rain storm—sunshine or a rainbow (contrasting light or weather)

3. a seedling—a mighty oak or a redwood tree (contrasting size)

4. a baby—a grandparent (contrasting age)

Exercise 2.2 (p. 32)

1. a kitten—a. soft, fluffy fur b. sandpaper

2. a new dress—a. clean, ironed, or brightly colored b. dirty, wrinkled, or faded

3. an athlete—a. boxing glove or spiked track shoe b. baby mitten or baby bootie

Exercise 2.3 (p. 35)

1. a. item—new shoes; b. reason—blister on foot; c. speech—"Why did you tempt me to buy you?"

2. a. item—broken TV; b. reason—favorite program is on; c. speech—"How come you always break when I need you the most?"

Exercise 2.4 (p. 35)

1. Item—George Washington—a. Where did you and Martha meet? b. Were your false teeth really made of wood? c. How did that cherry tree story get started? d. Did your legs get cold in those knee length pants?

2. Item—soaring eagle—a. Is it cold up there? b. What happens if you are scared of heights? c. You are a great symbol for the United States! d. Do you ever get dizzy up that high?

Exercise 2.5 (p. 38)

1. Buying a new car; Element: price; Hyperbole: It cost an arm and a leg just to look at it!

2. Food in the cafeteria; Element: long waiting line for meals; Hyperbole: That line was ten miles long.

3. First day of school; Element: New students; Hyperbole: There were a zillion kids I never saw before!

4. The first day of summer vacation; Element: Summer job; Hyperbole: I'm going to make a million dollars mowing lawns this summer.

Exercise 2.6 (p. 38)

1. That baby was so ugly that the clocks stopped!

2. That test was so long that I wore three inches off my pencil writing answers.

3. The track star was so fast that he melted the bottoms of his sneakers.

Exercise 2.7 (p. 41)

1. "That dress . . . (a) irony: A patient in a hospital gown sees himself in the mirror.
   (b) not irony: A passerby sees a gorgeous new dress in fashion store window.

2. "I love . . . (a) irony: fingernail scrapes on the chalkboard. (b) not irony: playing favorite CD.

3. "I'm happy to meet you." (a) irony: I meet Godzilla. (b) not irony: I meet my idol.

4. "My date book . . . (a) irony: The pages are all blank. (b) not irony: Owner has many engagements written on every page.

Exercise 2.8 (p. 41)

1. getting grounded—"Just what I've always wanted!"

2. a boring speech—"Call the network, this guy is ready for Prime Time."

3. a screaming baby—"What a cute baby—so calm and quiet."

4. a really hard test— "Hey, it was a piece of cake!"

Exercise 2.9 (p. 44)

1. weakness —(a) Bambi (b) I knew I had to help when he looked at me with those Bambi eyes.

2. beauty—(a) Venus (b) When she tried on the prom dress, she was Venus with arms.

3. anger—(a) Jaws (b) He targeted the thief like Jaws after prey.

Exercise 2.10 (p. 44)

1. Tarzan—(a) jungle vines (b) Mike without a phone was like Tarzan without a vine.

2. Sherlock Holmes—(a) detective, solves crimes (b) I knew I'd been caught when I saw Mom's Sherlock expression.

Exercise 2.11 (p. 47)

1. sunrise; element—light or new dawning

2. an owl; element—nocturnal nature or wisdom

3. a trumpet; element—sharp sound or brassy look

Exercise 2.12 (p. 47)

1. freedom: symbol—an eagle

2. neatness: symbol—a pin

Metaphor—(using owl—nocturnal nature from above) Jamie was a night owl who prowled until dawn.

Exercise 2.13 (p. 50)

1. (a) Billy, hit (b) the bullet hit the deer, not Billy

2. (a) Jane, flat (b) Jane's tire is flat, not Jane

3. (a) radio said (b) the announcer said, radio just transmitted his voice

Exercise 2.14 (p. 50)

1. Pentagon—The Pentagon paved the new parking lot.
2. White House—The White House announced a new policy.
3. Olympics—The Olympics tested all the athletes for drugs.

Exercise 2.15 (p. 53)

1. open—closed
2. alert—sleepy
3. bored—interested

Exercise 2.17 (p. 56)

Hurricane—The hurricane found the island.
Hot dog—The hot dog lured me to the table.

Exercise 2.18 (p. 56)

1. New CD—The new sound track begged for my attention.
2. Bed—His bed welcomed and soothed him.
3. Shadow—The shadow jumped from the corner and grabbed her.
4. Cup—The cup leaped out of my hand when I scared it with my yell of pain.

Exercise 2.19 (p. 59)

1. As fast as a student's alibi. OR a teacher's question.
2. Smelled like a forgotten wet bathing suit after a week. OR a runner's dirty socks.
3. Hurt like a broken prom date. OR being the last player chosen.
4. As fresh as a flirting sophomore. OR advertising claims for a new soap.

5. As busy as a thumb on the control of a new video game. OR chattering teeth.

Exercise 2.20 (p. 59)

1. The idea was like a flame in her brain.
2. It was like she washed the memory from her thoughts.
3. The dawn brought colors to the sand like the sun had painted it.

Exercise 2.21 (p. 62)

1. Blue Collar; (a) All the blue collars had a holiday. (b) The shirt had a blue collar.
2. Gumshoe; (a)The gumshoe tracked down the crook. (B) The nurse bought a new pair of gumshoes for both quiet and comfort.

Exercise 2.22 (p. 62)

1. <u>Paper</u> Paper is both a major part of and the most visible part of a report.
2. <u>Mouthpiece</u> The verbal skills of a lawyer are necessary in the courtroom and the lawyer speaks for the defendant.
3. <u>Tube</u> The face of the picture tube is the most visible part of the TV set.
4. <u>Hard Hat</u> This type of protective headgear is required on construction sites.
5. <u>Striped Shirt</u> This pattern is distinctive and is worn by officials so they can be recognized immediately on the field of play.

Exercise 2.24 (p. 65)

<u>Pine needles</u>—at least a dozen
<u>Dog hair</u>—two or three